Living on Earth

A Guide to Help You Achieve
Health, Happiness, and Success

ROSER SEGARRA

To my mom, and Andrew, Joshua, and Elisabeth. I love you forever.

Table of Contents

A note from the author

I WAS BORN in Spain, the fifth daughter of six children, and I grew up in a small beach town.

In my teens I started to develop a great interest in self-help and spiritual books. I was bullied as a child and subsequently I struggled for many years. I wanted to find out how to gain more confidence, and overall I just wanted to feel better. I longed to understand the bigger meaning in life. I felt there was more to it than just our bodies, but what was it?

While I was trying to figure it all out I went to University and I received a degree in Business Administration. After graduating, I left Spain with the intent to travel for about a year, to work, and to improve my English. I landed in Scotland, which I loved, and got a job as an accounts assistant. This position led to other opportunities and to my current career in accounting.

While in Scotland, I continued reading heavily all types of self-help, personal growth, and spiritual books while I also pursued becoming an Associate Chartered Management Accountant (ACMA).

I learned a lot during my stay in Scotland. Many of those spiritual books helped me gain confidence, understand the spiritual laws of creation, and manifest the lifestyle and career that I wanted.

Toward the end of my stay in Scotland, after 11 years, and shortly after I had my first child, I took an opportunity to relocate to Houston and work as a Chief Financial Officer (CFO) for an Oil and Gas Energy Company. Most recently, I held the role of Vice President of Finance.

My love for reading continues to this day. It has greatly helped me in my path to change my circumstances for the better and heal my emotional issues.

I have compiled everything I have learned in the past 25 years in this book, in the hope that it can help you too.

I wish you the very best on your path.

Roser Segarra
Houston, April 2017

Introduction

THIS BOOK STARTED in my head a long time ago. It reflects the knowledge I have gathered over the past 25 years reading and researching books on self help, spirituality, personal growth, and healing the body and soul. This knowledge has helped me make more sense of my life experiences, learn how to change my circumstances for the better, and live a happier existence.

I have learned that humanity is not a random accident, that there is a reason why we are here, and that each one of us has a purpose in life we have come to fulfill, a reason and purpose which we planned prior to incarnating. We are much more than our physical body; we are eternal souls incarnated in a body.

Our souls are units of consciousness that once upon a time belonged to an overall mass of consciousness, and this mass split up for the purpose of experiencing itself. All individual souls were created the same, from the same mass. From a physical perspective, our souls are higher aspects of ourselves that know we are spiritual bodies living a human experience, but our conscious self has forgotten this. We are simply energy and thus can't die, only change form.

We come to Earth repeatedly through the process of reincarnation. The Law of Reincarnation gives a soul the choice to come back to Earth if there is anything unresolved, or incomplete at the end of a lifetime, that the soul wants to take care of. The soul might have already been incarnated on Earth, and has a wide spectrum of soul family and karmic ties it wants to resolve, or it might be the first time it is incarnating.

Before our soul incarnates in a human body on Earth, it understands that:

1. Everything is Energy. We are vibrational beings, living in a vibrational universe that is contained in The All, or the Field of Consciousness.

Every human being and every place has its own unique vibrational resonance. This is the vibration, or atmosphere you feel when you go into a bar, enter a cathedral, or meet a person for the first time.

Everything in the universe also radiates a specific frequency (or vibration), which remains recorded permanently in what is called the Field of Consciousness. This field is a web of energy that connects our bodies and all beings in the world. All events, thoughts, feelings, and attitudes are recorded forever and can be retrieved at any time in the present or the future. Sir David R. Hawkins found a way to calibrate this phenomenon via kinesiology. We will explore this further in Chapter 2.

Our vibration is further refined as we evolve and grow in consciousness over many lifetimes, and with our thoughts and actions while on Earth.

Thoughts are measurable pure energy. Whether positive or negative, our thoughts create an emotional response in all the millions of cells in our body, which results in a powerful bodily vibration. When we have positive thoughts and feelings, the vibration is high; when negative, the vibration is low. Every thought we have, ever had, and will ever have, is creative. The energy of our thoughts never dies. As we think, we vibrate, and as we vibrate, we attract. A thought was the beginning of Creation.

2. Our soul understands it will inhabit a human body to evolve physically, emotionally, mentally, and spiritually. We will evolve when we master our life lessons, grow in consciousness, and remember who we are.

We grow in consciousness through taking on challenging experiences in physical form, which cause us to make important decisions and discover our inner resources.

Our soul knows it won't have to figure it all out on its own. Our soul receives assistance from the connection it keeps to the part that is not incarnated – our higher self. This is the part of us that remains on the other side of the veil. It is the essence of who we are and holds the accumulated knowledge from all our lifetimes. We don't come with 100% of our energy; we only bring as much as we think we will need in this incarnation. This connection to our higher self is frequently referred to as our intuition, although it also assists with what we call synchronicity. This is how we meet our significant partners and friends, or have unexpected amazing things happen to us. This connection is possible because of the existence of a universal Field of Consciousness (more about this field in Chapter 1).

Our evolved higher self is our spirit, the broader part of us that knows who we truly are. Our intuition is our higher self talking to us via our emotions; it is not generated from the brain. Have you ever looked at something that gave you the chills, or felt a sudden sunken gut feeling? That is your intuition talking to you, giving you signals as to what you need to know.

Our emotions are not random occurrences, they also tell us if our thoughts at any given moment are a vibrational match to how our higher self perceives us; that is, to what our higher being knows as being the truth. This is the reason we feel awful when we think, "I don't amount to anything," or "I'm so ugly." Our higher self knows that it is not true, and it is giving us the corresponding emotion of feeling awful so we are able to realize that. When we think a thought that rings true with who we really are, we feel harmony, joy, love, and a sense of freedom. When we think thoughts that don't ring true with who we are, we feel disharmony in our body, depression, and fear.

Our higher self knows our life plan and who we want to become, and via our emotions and intuition it is giving us clues as to which direction we need to follow in order to evolve and achieve our goals. We use this tool many times, although perhaps unconsciously. We conclude: "I didn't do it because it didn't feel right," yet we have no logical explanation for how we came to that decision.

It is the power of your intuition, not your logic, that will help you discern if the information provided in this book is right for you or not. It will *feel* right, or not. Your emotions and excitement will give you the answer.

As well as the connection to our higher self, our soul knows that from the moment it is born in physical form it will have the assistance and company of guides and angels.

3. Our soul understands that before incarnating, with the assistance of our guides and soul family members, we will have a *planning session* (more on this in Chapter 4), where we will plan the details of our upcoming life and our soul contracts and agreements with other people. We will also select the family we will be born to and our life challenges and circumstances, but once born – on a conscious level – we will forget all about it. This is known as *the Veil of Amnesia*, or *the Veil of Illusion*.

One of the biggest hurdles we will encounter on Earth is that we have forgotten who we really are and why we are here, and therefore we have to deal with the pain and suffering of why bad things happen to us and why we deserve our fate. If we remembered where we came from we would be longing to go back, and we would not be able to recognize what an opportunity for our soul's growth it is to be on

Earth. On the other side of the veil we ask for numerous opportunities to reincarnate until we feel we have completed our evolution.

4. While on Earth, our soul understands it will be governed by spiritual laws but it will also be provided with Free Will. Our thoughts will be the tool that will allow us to manifest our life plan, assisted by our intuition, guides, and angels.

We will set our ideal environment and all our main contracts and agreements before coming to Earth. However, it is while on Earth that we will create our experience by following the universal spiritual laws – consciously or unconsciously – along with our ability to change our mind with our given Free Will.

Free Will means that we will be able to be, do, and have what we want, and also, we will have the option to follow or not to follow our life plan and our agreed soul contracts. Although it might seem otherwise, we understand that earth won't be chaos and things won't happen at random. We will not be at the mercy of fate.

Two of the most popular and well-known universal spiritual laws are the Law of Karma and the Law of Attraction. We will delve into the implications of these laws in our daily lives in Chapters 6 and 7.

At some point in our lives, most of us will start searching for answers, wanting to know why we came to Earth, what is the purpose of being here. Our higher self will keep nagging us to search and find out what it is all about. Our soul knows we deserve love, fulfillment, and joy by birthright. If we have a dream, a goal, or a wish that we haven't fulfilled, it will keep reminding us. Repeatedly.

◆ ◆ ◆

This book is organized in three parts:

In Part I: In the Beginning, we will explore our spiritual self and the information we need to understand about our soul and our true nature. Specifically, we will learn about the Field of Consciousness that surrounds us and keeps us connected to our higher selves. We will learn about the planning sessions and the contracts that our souls agree to with other family members before coming to Earth, and we will discuss the evolution of our souls, from infancy to old age.

In Part II: Being on Earth, we will learn the tools to be able to live joyfully and successfully while being incarnated on Earth. Specifically, we will learn about the Spiritual Laws that govern our universe, giving particular attention to the Law of Karma, the Law of Attraction, and the Laws of Creation (the Law of Intention, the Law of Request, and the Laws of Faith and Attachment).

We will understand how to find our life purpose, and we will learn which tools will help us achieve our dreams to live a happier, more fulfilling, and more prosperous life on Earth. For example, we will learn how to use the power of our mind to create, how our thoughts impact everything around us, the difference between balancing and releasing karma, the role of gratitude, the power of goal setting, how to take responsibility for our lives, how not to sabotage our own manifesting, and much more.

In Part III: Healing Body and Soul, we will explore the tools to find harmony and health in the human body, physically and emotionally. First of all, we will learn about alternative therapies, the importance of conventional therapies, and how to choose the most appropriate therapy for us. We will also learn self-healing tools available to us, including the power of our mind to heal, the role of adequate nutrition, why diets don't work, what we can do to lose weight, and the role of exercise in our quest to lose weight.

Finally, we will finish Part III looking at how we can find long lasting healing in our bodies by learning how to heal difficult relationships and ultimately how to heal our inner wounds.

I have resolved my biggest emotional issues with the knowledge and understanding that I have gained over the years. Along the way, I have also learned a lot of things in the areas of career, manifesting the lifestyle I want, and maintaining my health, which have greatly helped me. I have bundled it all together in this book and it is my hope that it can be of assistance to you too.

My intention for this book is not to delve deeply into any particular subject but to provide an overall useful view and understanding of many subjects. Because I cover many topics, at one point I considered splitting this book in two; however, I believe you will get much more value and it will be more convenient if you have it all in one place.

I consider this book a stepping stone or path to more knowledge. For that reason, should you wish to deepen your knowledge further in a particular subject, this book contains many book recommendations.

Primarily, I recommend books because that is where I have gained most of my knowledge; however, you can also find a lot of free information on the Internet. I don't personally know any of the authors I'm recommending nor do I have any financial gain in recommending their classes, blogs, or books. If I recommend anybody, any therapy, or any book, it is because I like it, it has worked for me, and I think it will be useful for you too.

Part I
In the Beginning

1

The Field of Consciousness

In truth, there is only one mind

ERWIN SCHRÖDINGER,
1933 PHYSICS NOBEL PRIZE WINNER

EVERYTHING IN THIS universe is made up of energy and radiates a specific frequency that remains permanently in what is called the *Field of Consciousness*, a web of energy that connects everything in the universe. We are all part of this energy exchange; our energy is constantly interacting with the field.

All events, thoughts, feelings, and attitudes are recorded forever. This universal field is full of information that can be retrieved and repeatedly called upon at any time, in the present or in the future. This is because our consciousness is not stored in our brain; instead, our brain is a receiver that picks up the signal of our consciousness from the field. It is through this field that we are connected to all life.

This field has many names in different literature but refers to the same concept: The All, the Universal Mind, the One Mind, the Collective Unconscious, the Field of Consciousness.

The concept of the existence of a Field of Consciousness has been well documented by many authors.

In 1908, a book called *The Kybalion* was published by the Yogi Publication Society, written by a person or persons under the pseudonym of "Three Initiates." It contains the essence of the verbal teaching traditions of Hermetic Principles which describe the underlying laws of the universe. This book contains 7 Sacred Principles of Manifestation. The first sacred principle, called *Mentalism*, explains that the universe is composed of an all encompassing Divine Mind, its thoughts, and thought forms. This Divine Mind includes all individual minds: thoughts, emotions, feelings, and cognition. Our highest self is an extension of that Mind.

Mentalism contains the idea that "All Is Mind."

Larry Dossey, author of *One Mind: How Our Individual Mind Is Part of a Greater Consciousness and Why It Matters*, explains that the concept of the One Mind is ancient, and it remains an honored belief in many wisdom traditions. He writes, "The esoteric sides of all the major religions recognize that our individual consciousness is subsumed and nourished by an infinite, absolute, divine, or cosmic source, and is ultimately one with it."

He describes our mind as immortal and eternal, not confined to our brain or body but extending infinitely outside of it.

We can see the power of the field at work in the classic example of a mother who "just knows" her child is in danger, or between siblings who feel each other's pain. Numerous studies have tested this phenomenon in which people often exchange thoughts and emotions at a distance. The link is proven very strong in cases where hurt is involved, like a calling from one to another.

We are all connected in this field, and you have probably been aware of it, or felt it. Have you ever felt you were being watched, only to turn around and see that somebody was staring at you?

Nature is also in constant telepathic communication through the field. For example, some studies show how pets will go to wait at the door when their owner (who is away from home) shows intent to go home. It can also be observed that large groups of animals, herds, and flocks frequently behave in highly coordinated ways, implying a shared, overlapping mind.

Rupert Sheldrake, Ph.D., a British biologist, researcher, and author, has studied this phenomenon extensively. You can find a lot of free articles and information on his website[1]. He proposes that memory is inherent in nature and that natural systems, such as termite colonies or fish schools, inherit a collective memory from all previous things of their kind. He explains that animal telepathy is a consequence of the way animal groups are organized by what he calls *Morphic Fields*.

Sheldrake explains how detectives are sometimes trained not to stare too often or intently at the back of people they are following, so as not to provoke the individual to turn around, and that celebrity photographers report similar experiences. Celebrities being secretly photographed up to half a mile away often turn around and look down the lens of the camera. Hunters and wildlife photographers report similar experiences: animals seem to know when they are being stalked, turning toward the telescopic sight of the camera.

In *The Sense of Being Stared at*, Sheldrake suggests that through our *attention* we create fields of perception that stretch out around us, connecting us to what we are looking at. Through these fields, the observer and the observed are interconnected. Mental fields that extend beyond the brain may also help explain telepathy.

His experiments and findings in the subject are described at length in his books. If you want to read more about this, you might want to begin with *The Sense of Being Stared at: And Other Unexplained Powers of Human Minds*, and *Dogs Know When Their Owners Are Coming Home*.

---

[1] http://www.sheldrake.org

Another author who has written extensively about the field is Gregg Braden.

In his book, *The Divine Matrix: Bridging Time, Space, Miracles and Belief,* Braden explains the existence of a field of energy which he calls *The Divine Matrix,* which connects all creation and is the bridge between our inner and outer worlds. This field plays the role of a container for the universe to exist within, it seems to have intelligence, and is able to respond to the power of human emotion.

Braden postulates that because everything exists within the Divine Matrix, all things are connected, so what we do in one part of our lives must have an effect and influence on other parts. He also proposes that we are connected not only with everything we see in our lives today, but also with everything that's ever been, as well as with things that haven't happened yet.

◆ ◆ ◆

Because we are part of this Universal Mind, we can't always control the thoughts that enter our head. You might have started a conversation on a topic when somebody exclaimed they were thinking the same thing. When somebody has a thought, it circulates, and it is not long before somebody else in close proximity has the same thought. That's why we should be conscious of what we think and what we say; we can choose to send out positive or negative vibrations through the way we think and feel.

This really sums up what the Law of Attraction is about. If we think positive thoughts and have positive feelings, we are sending out positive vibrations, which in turn will attract experiences (and thoughts) of matching vibrations. Like attracts like. We have complete control over what thoughts stay in our head so every time we change our thoughts we can change our experience, the more positive the better. We will discuss the Law of Attraction further in Chapter 7.

Have you ever gone into a room full of people and felt the tension? It is likely that you were picking up many conflicting and angry thoughts. That is why it feels so good to be around uplifting, positive people, and so bad to be around negative people; the negativity literally gets in our heads and we feel it in our bodies. It is also physically detrimental for the negative person to perpetuate this behavior for long periods of time.

Connecting with the field is important because in the field resides all the synchronistic events and all the answers to the questions we have. Our higher self knows what we came to accomplish on Earth and who we need to meet in order to achieve it. When we put a request out, for example, a question about an issue, our higher self will tap into the field and through our intuition and emotions (with an image, a thought, or a gut feeling to go somewhere or do something), it will provide the answer.

The dreams we have are all definitely possible for us to achieve this lifetime; we would not have them if we could not make them a reality.

We will only be able to retrieve information from the field that reflects our level of consciousness and intent. If we mean well and our intent is pure, we will get information that vibrates at that level. If we mean to hurt or harm another, we will only receive muddled up, sick thoughts, because those will be the thoughts that vibrate at low levels of hate.

This is why some psychics are very good and some are not. All "readings" done, either through intuition, angel or tarot cards, or through any other type of psychic phenomena such as channeling, are only as good as the psychic's consciousness and intent. Genuine psychics who intend to help you (and with your permission) will be able to tap and retrieve the information you need. Psychics who just want to get your money, or show off "their gifts," will not get accurate information. If you want to visit a psychic your intuition will guide you to choose effectively. You always know when something or someone doesn't feel right.

Carl Jung, Swiss psychiatrist and psychoanalyst who founded analytical psychology, coined the phrase *Collective Unconscious*, referring to a subconscious pool of all the shared experiences of the human race. He considered the collective unconscious to underpin and surround the unconscious mind. Such a database comprises all of the information ever available to human consciousness and is the origin of all information obtained by intuition, premonition, divination, or dream.

In *The Significance of Constitution and Heredity in Psychology* (November 1929), Carl Jung writes:

> *The collective unconscious comprises in itself the psychic life of our ancestors right back to the earliest beginnings. It is the matrix of all conscious psychic occurrences.*

The existence of what Jung termed *Collective Unconscious* represents this Field of Consciousness, and what psychic phenomena is all about. The Law of Attraction and the Law of Karma regulate this exchange of information. We will delve more into the implications of these laws in Chapters 6 and 7.

On a side note, John Edward[2] is a brilliant psychic and medium. I first learned about him when I read his very touching book *One Last Time: A Psychic Medium Speaks to Those We Have Loved and Lost*. Edward connects with the souls of those human beings who have passed away. I recommend that you go to see him live in one of his shows if you ever have a chance. It will show you how real is the existence of life after death. We will explore the process of death and birth in Chapter 3.

◆ ◆ ◆

We can connect to the field by listening to our intuition while meditating, walking in nature, doing some creating endeavors such as painting or cooking, and being in silence.

---

[2] https://www.johnedward.net

If you wish to read about the field further, I recommend:

- *The Source Field Investigations: The Hidden Science and Lost Civilizations Behind the 2012 Prophecies*, by David Wilcock
- *The Sense of Being Stared at, and Other Unexplained Powers of Human Minds*, by Rupert Sheldrake
- *One Mind: How Our Individual Mind Is Part of a Greater Consciousness and Why It Matters*, by Larry Dossey
- *The Divine Matrix: Bridging Time, Space, Miracles, and Belief*, by Gregg Braden
- *The Field: The Quest for the Secret Force of the Universe*, by Lynne McTaggart

2

Calibrating the Field

To become more conscious is the greatest gift anyone can give to the world; moreover, in a ripple effect, the gift comes back to its source.

DAVID R. HAWKINS, IN *POWER VERSUS FORCE*

S IR DAVID R. Hawkins, MD., Ph.D., is a nationally renowned psychiatrist, physician, researcher, spiritual teacher, author, and lecturer. His research findings have been published widely in medical, scientific, and psychoanalytic journals.

Dr. Hawkins has found a way to calibrate the field using kinesiology, or muscle testing. In his book, *Power Versus Force: The Hidden Determinants in Human Behavior*, he explains that all events in the universe are recorded in a Field of Consciousness beyond time, locality, and the recall of memory. This record is then retrievable forever by a simple physiological phenomenon called *muscle testing*. He is then able to determine the truth or falsehood of any statement.

The muscle testing response is a simple "yes" or "no" to a specific stimulus. It is usually done by a person holding out an extended arm, and the tester pressing down on it, using light pressure.

Usually, the test person holds something to be tested in the hand of the other arm; for example, an envelope with a statement inside.

The tester tries to press the arm down, and says to the person, "Resist." If the item to be tested is beneficial to the person (or true), the arm will remain strong with the recognition of truth; the person is able to resist the pressure. If it is not beneficial, has an adverse effect, or doesn't have existence within the field, the arm will go weak; the arm of the person is unable to resist the pressure (in this case, the envelope might contain a false statement).

Through kinesiology calibrations taken over 20 years, Hawkins analyzed the whole spectrum of human consciousness, on a scale from one to 1,000, and created a profile of human experience which he calls *the Map of Consciousness.* Levels under 200 are considered to be "false": destructive, draining, depleting of energy, and temporary. Levels over 200 are considered to be "true": self-sustaining, constructive, energizing, and invincible.

The energy calibration of various states of awareness (from one to 1000), can be found at the *Consciousness Calibration Research Technique Blog* (CCTR Blog).[3]

At the low end of the scale are qualities such as guilt (30), fear (100), racism (110), revenge (150), and actions like bull fighting (35) or hunting wild animals (30). At higher levels over 200 are tolerance (245), cooperation (480), and Zen Buddhism (890).

With muscle testing, we should be able to tell the truth from falsehood about anything anywhere in time or space. The test itself proves to be independent of personal opinion or belief, and it doesn't matter if the person being tested is a child or an adult. The response was also the same whether a statement was vocalized or made silently. The results were predictable, repeatable, and universal. The higher the level of consciousness of the team, the more accurate the results were.

----

[3] http://www.ccrtblog.com/full-list/

It is important to note that both the *intention* of the tester and the one being tested have to calibrate over 200 to obtain accurate responses.

Hawkins claims that this technique provides people the means by which to calibrate levels of truth and determine whether they are being misled in any situation.

The implications of this simple procedure extend into law, criminal justice, psychotherapy, politics, medicine, and beyond.

The Cleve Backster experiment

Dr. Cleve Backster was an interrogation specialist for the Central Intelligence Agency (CIA) who accidentally discovered, using a polygraph (a lie detector), that plants:

1. Have high-level emotional activities similar to those of human beings.
2. Can detect and respond to human emotions.
3. Are also connected to their environment via the field.

Backster had many polygraphs on hand because he directed a polygraph examiner school.

In his first experiment, Backster was just curious to find out if he could measure the rate at which water rose from the root area of a plant into the leaf while watering it. Nothing much happened. He then decided to insert a leaf that was neighboring the electroded leaf, into a cup of hot coffee. There was no noticeable chart reaction. After 14 minutes of elapsed chart time, he had this thought: as the ultimate plant threat, he would get a match and burn the plant's electroded leaf.

In his book, *Primary Perception: Biocommunication with Plants, Living Foods, and Human Cells*, Backster explains that the very moment the imagery of burning that leaf entered his mind, the polygraph recording pen moved rapidly to the top of the chart. No words were spoken, no touching the plant, no lighting of matches; just his clear intention to burn the leaf. The plant recording showed dramatic excitation.

This discovery lead to his theory of *Primary Perception*, in which he claims that plants feel pain and have extrasensory perception (ESP). He believes that all living things (plants, animals, bacteria, and humans) are telepathic and in communication with one another.

This communication is possible thanks to the existence of a Field of Consciousness.

3

Reincarnation:
The Process of Death and Birth

*Fear of death and ignorance of the afterlife are fueling the
destruction of our environment that is threatening all of our lives. So
isn't it all the more disturbing that people are not taught what death is,
or how to die? Or given any hope in what lies after death, and so what
lies behind life? Could it be more ironic that young people are so highly
educated in every subject except the one that holds the key to the
entire meaning of life, and perhaps to our very survival?*

SOGYAL RINPOCHE,
THE TIBETAN BOOK OF LIVING AND DYING

The word *reincarnation* derives from the Latin, literally meaning "entering the flesh again." The Law of Reincarnation gives a soul the choice to come back to earth if there is anything unresolved or incomplete at the end of a lifetime that the soul wants to take care of. Our soul is given this option to accelerate our learning process and achieve greater levels of consciousness.

Rebirth is a key concept found in major Indian religions and in ancient Sanskrit texts of Buddhism, Hinduism, and Jainism. In

Judaism, the book of Zohar, first published in the 13th century and containing the wisdom of the Kabbalah, discusses reincarnation at length.

In the Buddhist approach, life and death are seen as one whole, where death is the beginning of another chapter of life. Death is a mirror in which the entire meaning of life is reflected. Tibetans divide our entire existence into four continuously interlinked realities:

1. Life
2. Dying and death
3. After death
4. Rebirth

The Tibetan Buddhist tradition has concentrated more attention on helping the dying person cross the borders of death than any other living religious tradition.

In the West, the work of Michael Newton Ph.D., provides one of the most comprehensively researched sources of information I have found on reincarnation, what happens to us when we die, what transpires between lives, and how we planned every detail of our future reincarnation on Earth. He is considered a pioneer in uncovering the mysteries of life after death through the use of hypnotherapy regression techniques.

Michael Newton holds a doctorate in Counseling Psychology, is a certified Master Hypnotherapist, and is a member of the American Counseling Association. He has been a hypnotherapist for over 50 years and a Life Between Lives (LBL) therapist for over 40 years.

Dr. Newton discovered, via hypnotic age-regression techniques, that many of his patients were able to recall past-life memories as well as the planning time spent between reincarnations. With the help of his patients, Dr. Newton has documented in detail all the stages of death and birth.

His findings can be found in his bestseller books, *Journey of Souls: Case Studies of Life Between Lives; Destiny of Souls: New Case Studies of Life Between Lives;* and *Life Between Lives: Hypnotherapy for Spiritual Regression.*

The stages of death and rebirth

The steps outlined below reflect a summary of the decades of work that Dr. Newton and many other researchers and authors have revealed. (Please see the recommended reading section at the end of this chapter.)

All authors have noted similarities among patients' descriptions of the afterlife, ultimately putting together a picture of the process the soul goes through from the moment his physical body dies to the moment he is reborn, which I have summarized as follows. (Note: Most authors use the term "subject" for their patients or participants. I am not sure if every person they regressed was always a patient, or a participant in their research. For the purposes of this book I have kept the same nomenclature of "subjects".)

1. **Death.** Most subjects recall looking down at their body and seeing people mourning over their death. They also recall their frustration at their attempts to talk to living people who don't respond. The subjects report seeing a tunnel and a pull toward a light, and a euphoric sense of freedom and brightness around them. When reaching the light, they see beautiful visions, music, and scenery, and they are greeted by what they describe as luminous beings, usually guides and deceased family members.

Everyone who dies is able to make a decision as to how they wish to go on living, and where. If they say, "Yes, I will die," the soul will continue its journey to the spiritual realm. The silver cord, which is an energy cord that connects the soul with the physical body, is severed and ceases to exist. If they say "No," the soul will be sent back to the physical world instantly, arriving a nanosecond before it "died." This might look like a near miss, a sudden remission, a near death experience (NDE), or a surprising recovery.

The timing and circumstances of death are always perfect, although it might not seem that way at the time. We will choose to die when our life on Earth is complete, when we have accomplished what we came to do, and when we have experienced all we came to experience. We make this decision based on many factors, but feeling "complete" or not is the main one.

Most subjects report staying around their loved ones until after their funeral.

2. **Healing**. During this stage, the soul will shed any regret, sadness, or traumatic memories from its previous life by going through what subjects describe as a "shower of light." This renews and restores the soul's vibrancy to its original form. Not every soul needs a shower of light.

3. **Past Life Review**. Our souls choose how they wish to review the life they just exited in a number of settings, usually a library. In this stage, it appears that some less evolved souls, who have committed murders and other crimes, will analyze their actions with their guides and decide on a new path (reincarnation) almost immediately. Typically, this happens because the soul is very eager to make amends and heal its karma.

   The majority of the pioneers in this work allude to a further review done with the "elders" (or "wise ones"). The elders are described as loving and kind, and never judgmental.

   The feedback the soul receives is on the basis of his original intent with his choices, as much as his actions. His motivations are questioned but not judged or condemned.

4. **Reunion**. After the soul has completed the light shower, and has reviewed the life he just left, souls are collected and projected out to their final destinations to meet up with their soul family. Their soul family is made up of souls who are at a similar stage in their evolution and with whom they have

shared and will share earthly lives with. Once he meets up with these souls, they usually compare experiences and learn from each other.

We keep reincarnating with our soul family members over and over, playing various roles with each other, such as husband and wife, brothers and sister, parent and child.

5. **Life Selection** (more on this in Chapter 4: Pre-Birth Planning Sessions). Once the soul has reviewed his prior life, has spent time with his guides and soul family members, has decided what he wants to work on and feels ready to reincarnate, he moves to a large sphere of light where he is able to choose his next life path. Most subjects recall being in what looks like a huge cinema with large screens. The soul is able to see multiple paths and determine which path would be the most appropriate. He also has the ability to fast forward through the timeline to see critical events that will happen.

Some souls will choose greater challenges to experience, such as a disability or abuse. Oftentimes the hardest tasks we set for ourselves begin in our childhood.

Spiritually and intellectually, we seem to pick up where we left off. All our efforts to improve, grow spiritually, become a wiser and a better person, or excel at any discipline (music, sports, art) are recorded and retained in our soul, building on them from lifetime to lifetime. No effort is ever wasted. This is how child prodigies can be explained; the soul appears to be able to download information and talent into the developing physical body and mind.

6. **Preparation.** After the soul chooses the life path he feels is perfect for his next reincarnation, he then meets up with the souls who will play key roles in his next life. With the assistance of these souls he will do extensive planning, create synchronicities that will guide him throughout his lifetime, and he will make agreements to assist the completion of the lessons and tasks he will set out to master. Higher-level guides also help to plan out specific symbols that he will see or hear,

which will trigger certain thoughts and actions at specific times.

Have you ever met someone for the first time, a person who will become important in your life, like a mentor or a spouse, and you felt at ease and a connection straight away? You might have been intrigued by their eye color, the necklace they were wearing, or some other physical aspect. You might have just *felt* they were right for you. Those are the cues we prepare before we arrive, so we can recognize each other.

7. **Rebirth (Return to Earth).** Subjects report traveling back to Earth through the same tunnel in which they left, entering the mother's womb.

   Upon birth, the Veil of Illusion (amnesia) drops again, although not completely. Many children remember past lives and have imaginary friends. For most people, all of that remembrance dissolves by the time they are about five years old.

   Dr. Ian Stevenson, former Professor of Psychiatry at the University of Virginia School of Medicine, and former chair of the Department of Psychiatry and Neurology, dedicated most of his career to finding evidence of reincarnation. He accumulated what is probably the best known collection of scientific data that appears to provide proof of reincarnation. He investigated many reports of young children who claimed to remember a past life. He conducted more than 2,500 case studies over a period of forty years and published twelve books, including *Twenty Cases Suggestive of Reincarnation* and *Where Reincarnation and Biology Intersect*. He claims to have found over 3,000 examples of reincarnation which he shared with the scientific community.

Some people wonder why the Veil of Illusion drops and why we need to forget our true origin. I have read varying points of view on that question, but basically it comes to this: If we remembered our origin and every detail of our life plan, coming to Earth would be the equivalent of sitting an exam when we already knew the questions. If you know your partner is going to die suddenly in his 40s, you will not be faced with the grief and shock and subsequent strength and healing that you might achieve if you were expecting it.

Although we might forget, it doesn't mean that we have to face Earth, and our undesirable experiences, all on our own. Not only we have our soul family members with us (who might or might not be supportive depending on the role they are playing), but once born everybody is assigned at least one spiritual guide who will assist the soul while living on Earth.

In Dr. Michael Newton's words[4]:

I find it interesting that the old-fashioned religious term of having a "guardian angel" is now used metaphysically to denote an empathetic spirit. To be honest, this is a term I once denigrated as being foolishly loaded with wishful thinking and representing an outdated mythology at odds with the modern world. I don't have that belief anymore about guardian angels.

Our guides and angels will always lend a helping hand, even if we don't believe in them.

The work of Dr. Brian Weiss

After reading the work of Dr. Newton, I became very interested in the subject of reincarnation, and I found that one of the pioneers of this work is Dr. Brian Weiss. Weiss graduated from Columbia University and Yale Medical School and is the former Chairman of Psychiatry at the Mt. Sinai Medical Center in Miami.

In his bestselling book, *Many Lives, Many Masters: The True Story of a Prominent Psychiatrist, His Young Patient, and the Past-Life Therapy that*

---

[4] *Journey of Souls*, Fith revised edition, 2003, Chapter 3

Changed Both Their Lives, Dr. Weiss explains his astonishment when one of his patients began to recall past life traumas. During one hypnosis session, his client introduced spirit guides who had been her soul therapists between lives.

Dr. Weiss explains that bumping into these past life traumas opened a can of worms for him because he didn't want to feel ridiculed by his peers; however, he felt he needed to share the message with the world. Dr. Weiss was Chief of Psychiatry and had already published 37 scientific papers and book chapters in his field. He said that it took him four years to write about what happened, to garner the courage to take the professional risk of revealing this unorthodox information. In his own words, "I knew that no possible consequence I might face could prove to be as devastating as not sharing the knowledge I had gained about immortality and the true meaning of life."

Since writing *Many Lives, Many Masters*, Dr. Weiss has also published several more books on the subject of reincarnation and life after death.

Near death experience (NDE)

If you wish to explore further the possibility of life after death, you might also want to read the testimonies of people who have experienced a near death experience (NDE). In most cases, the testimonials follow a common theme which can be summarized as follows:

1. Feeling of peace, no pain, and no fear. All of a sudden, they see themselves floating above their bodies, feeling great and able to see and hear what is happening "below." In many instances, after they come back "alive," they relay to their doctors and nurses the conversations they were having during their operation in the hospital or whatever the circumstances in which they were dying.

2. They are aware of another reality and see a tunnel, then a light in the distance, to which they are drawn. Some people meet their guides or other compassionate and loving light beings. Most of the times, there is some kind of telepathic conversation between them.

3. At some point they remember agreeing to go back to their body, and in some cases they also remember the reason why; typically, they have something unfinished to do. It can be anything from fulfilling a personal goal to supporting a family member.

Although some scientific communities provide reasons for NDEs – such as lack of oxygen to the brain which might result in hallucinations, excess carbon dioxide which might create the tunnel and vision of white light, or epileptic activity in the temporal lobes – the striking thing is that once they recover from an NDE, they don't go about their lives as they did before. The NDE feels very real and usually totally transforms the person who experienced it. They have less interest in obtaining material possessions but grow an interest in life and in all things spiritual, they feel a significantly reduced fear of death, and they worry much less over small things. Overall, they seek a bigger meaning in life.

◆ ◆ ◆

There are many books on the subject of reincarnation, life planning, and NDEs. My favorite authors and books are:

- Michael Newton: *Journey of Souls* and *Destiny of Souls*
- Robert Schwartz: *Your Soul's Plan* and *Your Soul's Gift*
- Brian Weiss: *Many Lives, Many Masters*
- Andy Tomlinson: *Exploring the Eternal Soul: Insights from the Life Between Lives*

- Anita Moorjani: *Dying to Be Me: My Journey from Cancer, to Near Death, to True Healing* (NDE)
- Todd Burpo: *Heaven Is for Real: A Little Boy's Astounding Story of His Trip to Heaven and Back* (NDE)
- Sogyal Rinpoche: *The Tibetan Book of Living and Dying.* This is an excellent book on the Tibetan traditions and their insights into life and death.

To close out this chapter I want to share a beautiful parable:

Life after delivery

In a mother's womb were two babies.
One asked the other: "Do you believe in life after delivery?"
The other replied, "Why, of course. There has to be something after delivery.
Maybe we are here to prepare ourselves for what we will be later."

"Nonsense," said the first. "There is no life after delivery.
What kind of life would that be?"

The second said, "I don't know, but there will be more light than here.
Maybe we will walk with our legs and eat from our mouths. Maybe
we will have other senses that we can't understand now."

The first replied, "That is absurd. Walking is impossible.
And eating with our mouths? Ridiculous! The umbilical cord
supplies nutrition and everything we need. But the umbilical cord is
so short. Life after delivery is to be logically excluded."

The second insisted, "Well I think there is something and maybe it's
different than it is here. Maybe we won't need this physical cord anymore."

The first replied, "Nonsense. And moreover, if there is life,
then why has no one ever come back from there? Delivery is the
end of life, and in the after-delivery there is nothing but
darkness and silence and oblivion. It takes us nowhere."

"Well, I don't know," said the second,
"but certainly we will meet Mother and she will take care of us."

The first replied "Mother? You actually believe in Mother?
That's laughable. If Mother exists, then where is She now?"

The second said, "She is all around us. We are surrounded
by Her. We are of Her. It is in Her that we live. Without Her
this world would not and could not exist."

Said the first, "Well, I don't see Her, so it is
only logical that She doesn't exist."

To which the second replied, "Sometimes, when you're in
silence and you focus and you really listen, you can perceive Her
presence, and you can hear Her loving voice, calling down from above."

AUTHOR UNKNOWN

4

Pre-Birth Planning Sessions

You only live once, but if you do it right, once is enough

MAE WEST

THE IDEA THAT we planned our life circumstances and experiences before we came to Earth totally changed my perception of life. Some of the struggles and difficult life events that had occurred to me as a child, and while growing up, started to make more sense.

In the previous chapter we saw that, at some point between lives, our souls will attend a "planning session." When we are not incarnated, we have the wisdom of the whole and we fully understand the implications of what we plan, especially when we give ourselves a seemingly difficult life.

Our soul will attend a planning session where it decides that coming to Earth is the ideal way forward to keep progressing on its evolution. Depending on the level of evolution of the soul (more on this in Chapter 5: Soul Evolution), this planning session might be very straightforward or very complicated.

A planning session

Each soul creates the life path that offers the best possibility for experiencing the emotions it seeks to understand and make peace with.

We don't always plan difficult lives, but our soul knows that with difficult assignments we will accelerate our growth and we will achieve our karmic goals faster. However, we will never set up unachievable goals or take on more than we can handle.

We make every choice with our highest interests in mind:

- We choose our timeframe in history, including location and exact date and time of day that we will be born.
- We choose our name, which will assist our soul's learning. The name is given by the soul to the mother and/or father telepathically. On rare occasions the parents might choose not to listen.
- We choose our parents, immediate family, and close friends (including our socio-economic class), and significant romantic and business partners. We often choose to reincarnate with the same family members (or group) but in different roles. A soul that was a sibling in a past life could be our daughter or father in this one.
- We choose if we will be adopted or be naturally born to our mother. There are various reasons why a soul might choose to come to Earth via adoptive parents. For example, the adoptive mother might know that her body will not be able to conceive, and requests a family soul member to be her adopted child in her next lifetime. The adopted child's soul might want to experience adoption or be of assistance to her soul. In most cases not having blood ties doesn't make the bond any weaker for they are still part of the same soul family.
- Within our family, we choose lineage intent. What that means is that we choose a family that will support our intent; for example, being born to a family with many generations of doctors if we wish to be one. Or quite the opposite, we choose a family that will not support our intent because one of

our primary life lessons is to stand up for ourselves and fight for who we want to become.

- We choose our gender and sexual orientation. Our soul is androgynous; it is probable that we will all choose to be either sex, man or woman, or gay or lesbian, at some point through our many reincarnations, because we learn the most through duality and experiencing both sides of the spectrum.

- We choose our physical attributes. The soul knows the health of the baby in the uterus. If the baby's health, or lack of, won't serve the souls purpose, then the soul will not choose that body and will choose another one. This includes genetic issues – being born with Down's syndrome or cystic fibrosis – or propensity issues, being thin or fat, having headaches, etc.

- We choose the main aspects we want to work on, such as tolerance, patience, poverty or wealth (in some cases, both poverty and wealth in the same lifetime), self-respect, or coping as a single parent.

  The Law of Balance and Polarity says that we are always seeking balance, and for that reason we experience opposites in order to learn from them. Some people are extremely wealthy or poor, generous or greedy, loving or unloving. By experiencing opposite sides of a spectrum over many lifetimes we aim at finding the perfect balance. Understanding this law and putting it into practice means that we can look inwardly to what aspects we think we are off balance and try to rectify them.

- In most cases we build some adversity into the life plan, along with the tools and people to assist and teach us. It is through our life challenges, and how well or badly we handle them, that our soul has decided to evolve. We will not have experiences that don't contribute to our knowledge and have not been agreed upon us. Lessons that have been learned in the past will not be presented again.

  Planning our lessons and adversities doesn't mean we are destined to experience all the fear and pain they might cause; suffering is not strictly necessary because we also planned the solution (in the form of mentors, understanding how to use our intuition, books, and knowledge). I think this is the reason we are seeing so many more spiritual and self-help books in the market, and why doctors such as Dr. Weiss and Dr. Newton are finding and releasing information about our pre-life choices. Although we will always have free will, we can also start having a deeper understanding of who we really are, how to take responsibility, and how to live a more joyous and fulfilling life. Instead of becoming suffocated by our circumstances, with this understanding we can heal and transform our challenges.

- We will make agreements with other souls who will help us master the main aspects we are going to work on. For example, our future partner might agree to leave us if we want to understand the challenge of coping as a single parent. He or she might also leave for a myriad of other reasons. We knew the potentials of everything we have gone through so far.

- We will also understand how major life events that we can't change are going to affect us; for example, the death of our parents or a close friend, or other events that will come at some point in our life. When they die, that is the perfect timing for their chosen path, and there is nothing we can do about it. But how we handle the situation is up to us.

- Our soul decides how much karma it will create and how much it will balance and release. It will make arrangements with the other souls involved in order to achieve this. (We also have free will, so we can choose to balance and release much more or less karma than we originally planned.) We will discuss the Law of Karma in Chapter 6.

- Last but not least, we define a number of exit points for when we will leave our human body, and when these points come up we will choose whether we wish to take them or not. Sometimes we plan our death to bring great blessings to the world or to make some kind of statement.

Life choices and agreements

Our souls plan painful experiences because in a broader sense our soul is unafraid of any challenge. We know that we can't get hurt because we are eternal and there is nothing that can happen that could threaten our soul. We know that our potential painful experiences will assist our soul's evolution and understanding in life. Sometimes we also want to balance and release karma.

As difficult as it might seem, all our experiences have a purpose and we have created them, either through pre-birth choice or while on Earth; otherwise, they wouldn't exist.

The following are some examples of pre-birth life choices and agreements.

Suicide

The option of suicide is sometimes contemplated as a way out in the pre-life planning session. The same way we run away from problems on Earth physically, like moving away to another city or country, or drinking or eating too much to alter our state of consciousness, sometimes we also choose an early exit from Earth. This is not good or bad; it is just another lesson that the soul wants to master on Earth.

Suicide is one of the many challenges that we bring with us throughout our lifetimes.

In some instances, the soul knows it always choses an early exit as a way to overcome its challenges, and repeatedly wants to put itself in the same situation, until it chooses not to commit suicide again.

The soul doesn't have to agree to anything in a planning session. Sometimes, the guides suggest easier and softer lifetimes to handle a specific issue; but the soul, because it wants to grow quickly, chooses a very difficult life again. The soul wishes to put behind a pattern he doesn't like; in this case, suicide. On a soul level we understand that the afterlife is all there is, and will always be there.

Suicide is by no means failure. Although it might seem that the soul didn't achieve the lesson it wanted to overcome, there are instances where the soul makes an agreement with his family members to die that way because of the huge amount of shock and guilt that will leave behind (he could have chosen a car accident, but didn't.) This is particularly relevant in the cases when a soul decides to incarnate in a physical body with a propensity to experience mental health issues. This health condition makes the option of suicide a logical path since the human body doesn't have adequate reasoning skills, and does not fully understand the consequences of his actions. The soul is helping soul family members with their own lessons.

The definition of suicide is "the act of intentionally causing one's own death," but we always choose when and how we die. Therefore, we could say that we always commit suicide. The issue is that the term *suicide* refers to an obvious, self-inflicted way of terminating our lives, for everybody to see and experience the consequences. Any other way of dying is also suicide (because we intentionally decide to leave), but we will call it an illness, an accident, or old age.

No human being will ever die without the agreement of its higher self. If the soul is not ready to leave Earth, then the physical body won't die. No death is ever wasted; nobody dies "in vain."

Losing children

I have learned there are many reasons why some souls choose a short lifetime. This is always done with the absolute love and agreement of all parties.

From the point of view of the thousands of lives we experience, dying while the human body is young is not viewed by the soul as a tragedy; the tragedy is on Earth because the family members who are left behind can't see their child's higher purpose and his or her next circle of reincarnation at that time.

Our souls are indestructible and wise, and we know what we are doing, even when it doesn't seem that way.

A common theme across all the books I have read on the subject is that babies and children (young and adult) die for a variety of reasons:

- To fulfill a contract with their mother or father (or both). Sometimes these children come with no karma and they agreed to come to their birth mother, and father (extending in some cases to many surrounding relatives) to assist them in their growth and evolution. For example, to help them put their lives into perspective and focus on what is really important. I have read many cases where the opposite happens: Both parents, or else just the mother or just the father, die young to follow a contract with their children; those children wish to experience growing on Earth without a parent or parents.
- To bring light and love to the area. When a child is sick, many uplifting prayers are sent to that child, house, and area. The child knows that. He also knows he can come back quickly if he wishes to do so.
- To assist a family member to embark on his or her life purpose. The sibling, cousin, parent, or family member might choose to become a doctor to find a cure for whatever illness the child died of, or to create a charity to help many other families in similar circumstances.
- To experience being in a womb and on Earth for a while.
- To be born in a healthier body. The soul realizes that the physical body of the baby is not growing or developing in the intended way, and it won't serve the soul's higher purpose; therefore, it chooses to leave. The soul will likely come back to the same parents later, waiting for the right circumstances to attach to a new pregnancy.

Robert Schwartz provides in his website a free PDF article[5] explaining the story of Valerie, who lost her only child and her fiancée in separate incidents. Valerie planned to go through both experiences before she incarnated. You can also read her story (and others) in Schwartz's amazing book *Your Soul's Plan*.

---

[5] Yoursoulsplan.com, http://bit.ly/2xaKpXg

More life choices and agreements

- Bump contracts. A person agrees to intersect at a moment in our life to check how we are doing and if we are following the path we set ourselves prior to birth. Sometimes we get distracted, or simply lost, or too depressed.

  These contracts often come with great intensity and leave a great mark in our lives; a short-term lover or a helpful friend who gives us the best advice we ever needed. It isn't always traumatic; but the experience will give us the opportunity to get back on the path we were supposed to be on (although we might not take it).

- Transition contracts. We made agreements with the souls of people who will help us cross over. This could be a nurse or a family member.

- Altruistic lives. This refers to lives planned solely to assist other human beings, a situation, and/or the earth. For example, dying at birth in a hospital that has questionable practices, or being born a girl in a country where she will be killed for not being a boy. The soul might have chosen that life to raise awareness.

- Choices made depending on soul evolution. Some very young souls come to Earth only for a brief period of time to experience life in a human body. In these cases, the soul might just choose a short life in a developing country and there is no more planning involved. Or an evolved soul that has had thousands of lives on Earth might only have a few lessons left to learn. If the soul chooses a longer life, the planning is much more complicated as there are only specific places, types of parents, times of the year, and many other attributes that would meet all of the soul's pre-birth requirements.

- Contracts with pets. We also make agreements with our pets prior to incarnating. Robert Schwartz has a (free) blog[6] about this. You can also find it in his book *Your Soul's Gift*. Schwartz shares the story of Marcia, who chose before coming into her body to be a dwarf. In this lifetime Marcia is but 1.4 meters (less than 5 feet) tall. Marcia knew before she was born that people would reject and dismiss her because of her height, so she built into her plan a safeguard: she would always have the unconditional love of her pets.

There are countless other agreements and lessons, like experiencing mental illness, parenting handicapped children, or being born with a disability, sexuality issues, drug addiction, anger management, and as many other challenges as you are able to think of.

Please see the recommended reading section at the end of this chapter if you wish to read more about pre-birth life choices and agreements.

We continue to make contracts once incarnated

Once on Earth, we are subject to the spiritual laws of the universe which we will discuss in Part II of this book. We create by following these laws, consciously or unconsciously, but we can also still make agreements with other souls in our sleep.

I'm recommending below what I perceive to be the best books should you wish to expand on this subject, but I have not found one single book that deals with one issue only. All the books that I have read cover a range of agreements and lessons. (The first two are repeated from Chapter 3, but they are also relevant for this chapter, and I have added their table of contents):

---

[6] Yoursoulsplan.wordpress.com http://bit.ly/2eJgvllI

- *Your Soul's Gift,* by Robert Schwartz:
  Table of contents: Healing, spiritual awakening, miscarriage and abortion, caregiving, pets, abusive relationships, sexuality, incest, adoption, poverty, suicide, rape, and mental illness.
- *Your Soul's Plan,* by Robert Schwartz:
  Table of contents: Physical illness, parenting handicapped children, deafness and blindness, drug addiction and alcoholism, death of a loved one, and accidents.
- *Memories of the Afterlife: Life Between Lives, Stories of Personal Transformation,* edited by Michael Newton, with case studies by members of the Newton Institute.
- *Same Soul, Many Bodies: Discover the Healing Power of Future Lives through Progression Therapy,* by Brian Weiss.

5

Soul Evolution

Claims of superiority are generally unenlightened.

THE JESHUA CHANNELINGS

MOST PEOPLE ARE familiar with the term *old soul*. What it usually means is that the personality of the person is showing some qualities of an advanced soul, such as compassion, knowledge, balance, and understanding of life.

Several books classify souls as beginner, intermediate, and advanced. Usually, the composition of a soul group (or soul family) is made up of beings on the same level of advancement. In *Journey of Souls*, Dr. Newton follows the same classification. However, in *Destiny of Souls*, after many more years of research, Dr. Newton writes about his discovery that souls will display energy color depending on their stage of evolution, or advancement, and thus he is able to ascertain their advancement level on that basis.

Newton discovered that white refers to younger souls, moving into yellow, orange, green, and finally the blue ranges. The deeper and richer colors referred to the most advanced souls. In addition to these center core auras, there are subtle mixtures of halo colors within every group that relate to the character aspects of each soul.

Dr. Newton classifies soul development as moving from a level one beginner through various learning stages to that of a master level six. (Other authors follow a very similar classification, from baby to old soul, which we will discuss later in this chapter.)

The soul advancement level refers to the consciousness and self-awareness within each soul. As the souls progress through each stage, they gain more experience and their consciousness expands. The evolution of our souls is marked by all the choices and decisions we have made over our many lives on Earth.

In the same way that a professor is not better than a student, or an older sibling is not better than a younger one, older souls are not "higher" or better than younger ones. It is the same energy with the same potential, but some souls progress more quickly and others more slowly. Some have had many thousands of lives on Earth and others haven't.

The best analogy I can think of would be this: Take, for example, all the ingredients we need for two cakes. We use the same exact ingredients and quantities, and the same quality flour. We put them both in the oven (Earth) and one cake comes out fully cooked, full of flavor, amazing. The other one comes out from the oven a bit too soon or undercooked, not that great. But they are both made of the same stuff, the same flour. The undercooked cake just needs to go back in the oven and cook a bit longer. It might have to go back many times, but at some point it will cook and will come out just as perfect as the first cake. In this analogy, the cake could get burned, and sometimes life on Earth becomes very hard going and we "burn out." But once we return to the spirit world, we recharge our batteries in the "shower of light" that we learned about in Chapter 2, and symbolically we go back in the oven until we come out good. But at no point are we any more or less of a cake, or flour. If the oven is not the perfect cooking tool any longer, the cake can also go to many other ovens (or planets).

The stage of a soul in his development is very useful when we try to understand people's behavior. When we say, "Well, he or she is thirty (or fifty); he should know better by now," the reality is that no, sometimes he won't know better because he is a young or an intermediate soul. Even old souls will have their own issues to resolve; otherwise, they wouldn't be here. Physical body age is beside the point.

Our soul progresses through the following stages of development: Infant, baby, young, mature, and old soul; but there is a gradual blend from one stage to the next. A person at the start of the mature stage, for example, will act mostly like a young soul but with some traits of a mature soul will begin to emerge.

Important note: This is just a guideline for understanding our soul evolution. It is not a hard and fast rule. A person might be portraying the characteristics of a young soul yet be an old one. Sometimes people don't fully evolve into who they really are until later on in life, or until they have experienced a traumatic or life changing event. The characteristics below are general guidelines.

Infant (or newborn) souls

Infant souls typically come to Earth for a few hours or weeks to experience the atmosphere of Earth. They also thrive in simple environments close to nature, such as tribes or rural settings. They possess a very simplistic view of life.

They might commit crimes without any sense of wrongdoing since they lack social understanding and experience on Earth. Most serial killers are infant souls.

Baby (or child) souls

Baby souls think much more about rights and wrongs, and they like to live within a set of rules. They seek order and stability in life, to the point of being too rigid. Both their beliefs and actions are rule bound, so they are usually ultra conservative, regimented, upright, and moralistic, with strong values.

If they break the rules they might self-torture with guilt and shame.

Young (or teenage) souls

Young souls are slightly more evolved but need clear direction and boundaries. They tend to be impetuous, self-centered, competitive, and rigid in their thinking. Sometimes they create bad karma because of their inability to use their excess energy constructively. They are strongly ego driven, looking for worldly fame and success. Note: There is nothing wrong with seeking fame and wanting to succeed in your field, but young souls will tend to show off their fame and wealth to everybody else once they "make it." It is their attitude and thinking that they are superior that makes them a young soul.

They have gone past most of the negative behavior that infant and baby souls possess, but they are still externally focused and have a way to go in other aspects.

Mature (or adult) souls

Mature souls are becoming wiser and are repaying debts they have built over the years. This is why sometimes they have very difficult lives. They are reaching a level of maturity that they didn't have before; therefore, at the planning sessions they will pick experiences that will challenge them, in order to grow and progress as fast as they can.

Mature souls tend to be more reflective than younger souls; they search for a bigger meaning in life. They seek to grow an understanding of themselves; spiritual growth becomes very important. They don't need to prove themselves and win at all costs. They can be competitive without the ego issue that younger souls have.

Old souls

Old souls are usually characterized by the fact that they possess knowledge and wisdom that is visible to others. Sometimes they take on caring roles, such as doctors and nurses, but they appear in all trades and places. An old soul might be a homeless person helping out baby, or younger souls that are homeless. Never judge any person or situation as you don't know what their soul is trying to accomplish.

Compared to younger souls, old souls are detached, compassionate, calm, and measured, humanitarian, and typically unattached to social structures and cultural expectations. They might be very wealthy, but they don't pursue materialist things for the sake of it.

Old souls come in all shapes and sizes, big and small, thin and fat, black and white, gay and lesbian. Old souls don't feel the need to defend their beliefs. They let go and let be.

Part II
Being on Earth

6

The Law of Karma

*Every Law has its Effect; every Effect has its Cause; everything
happens according to Law. Chance is but a name for Law not recognized;
there are many planes of causation, but nothing escapes the Law.*

THE KYBALION

OUR SOUL REINCARNATES on Earth with the
understanding that while on Earth we will be governed by
vibrationally based spiritual laws.

These laws have always existed, but most of the time we are
unaware of them. They offer order and justice in what it seems to be a
very dysfunctional world. These laws work regardless of religion,
beliefs, skin color, birthplace, social status, or any other attribute you
might think of. If you are living on Earth, then you are subject to
them.

Everything we do generates a force of energy that returns to us in
the same manner we sent it out. This is the Law of Karma. It is the
rule of cause and effect; no matter what, we reap what we sow.

The Law of Karma has been widely misunderstood. The universe
responds to our thoughts, feelings, and actions, it does not judge them

right or wrong, and does not deal in rewards or punishment, but in consequences. A consequence from our actions is just that, a natural outcome. You can earn good and bad karma, but the word *karma* per se is neutral (the same way that the word *money* is neutral, but you can use it for good or bad).

Karma is an opportunity to grow. It could be equated to the law of gravity; if you jump out of an airplane without a parachute you will plummet to the earth and most likely die. This is a consequence of your action of not putting on a parachute; it is not a punishment.

Karma is the energy carried over from former lifetimes regarding unfinished lessons, plus all karma that we create while living on Earth in this incarnation. Not every lifetime is of big karmic importance; we have many lifetimes lived as rest periods between the ones that are meaningful.

We have no one to blame or get credit for our karma. We are responsible for our actions, and we are responsible for how we react to other people's actions.

Difference between karma and life lessons

Karma is about situations with other humans, unfinished business, and unresolved issues that need completing; it is a system of interaction. Life lessons are totally and completely personal.

Life lessons can stay with us even after we have voided our karma; for example, when we need to work on not being judgmental, having patience, loving unconditionally, or not blaming others. Both karma and life lessons can be and are usually intermingled.

Sometimes we feel we can't get our act together and we experience the same lesson over and over, like attracting the "wrong type" of partner, or constantly running out of money. Although we might consciously want to overcome these patterns, on a subconscious level we might enjoy the attention that these situations generate. We might also need to tweak our beliefs and our constant repetitive statements to ourselves, for example, "I never have enough," or "I always attract the wrong type." The life lessons in these cases might be to step out of drama and to take responsibility for our lives.

The Law of Karma exists because our soul needs a just and fair way of understanding its actions. It is the spiritual way of getting things right, of being fair to every soul. The Law of Karma was created so we would understand the repercussions of our given free will.

The implications of our free will in our life plan are big because we can divert from the agreed upon plan as we wish. We are given the option to not follow through with our agreements, and in doing so we create and vibrationally attract experiences with positive and negative consequences.

The role of our emotions

Our emotions are the key to understanding the type of karma we are creating; they are not meaningless occurrences in our body. They are the most valuable tool to let us know how close or far away we are from creating what we want.

When we feel good, our higher self is telling us that it agrees with our perspective; if we feel bad, our higher self is not in agreement. For example; when we do or think of doing something "wrong," we will feel negative emotion. Our higher self is sending us a bad feeling to give us his perspective, such as "stealing won't assist your growth." On the other hand, when we help somebody in need, we feel great. That is because our higher self is telling us it is a good deed and we are going on the correct path.

The better we feel, the closer we are to everything our soul set out to achieve in this lifetime.

◆ ◆ ◆

The positive or negative results we seem to experience in our daily lives (sometimes termed as good and bad luck) are natural outcomes of all the spiritual laws, plus the results of the contracts we planned before we came to Earth.

There are various conditions that modify the strength of karma:

1. Persistent, repeated action.
2. Action done with great intention and determination. If our intent is to harm another, even if eventually we don't manage to hurt them but we still meant to do it, that intent is registered in our soul and the Field of Consciousness. The same applies to people with good intent. The old adage, "It's the thought that counts," is so true. Whether we mean well or not, it is always registered.
3. Action done without regret.

Balancing and releasing karma

Our soul will make arrangements with other souls – at the planning sessions and while on Earth – and will decide how much karma it will create and how much it will balance and release. There is a difference between balancing and releasing karma.

Karma is balanced when the soul feels it has experienced all sides of an issue. For example, it has killed and it has been killed and has fully learned from both aspects.

Karma is released when the underlying causes of the original imbalance are resolved. For example, if we killed because we disapproved of the other person's religion, or because someone didn't have the same skin color as we did, our soul will only fully release karma when it grows in consciousness and understands that all souls were created equal, and therefore all humans are equal. That is, it releases the belief that skin color, or the type of religion anybody belongs to, could make a person inferior or worthy of killing.

It is important we understand well the difference between balancing and releasing karma; unless we heal the underlying causes of our karma, we will tend to create new karma even after the original karma was balanced.

The idea that karma is always role reversal from lifetime to lifetime, or even while being on Earth, is not accurate. We don't always balance karma by experiencing the opposite; killers don't come back to be killed. For example, if we have made bad choices and hurt people, we might decide to put ourselves in the same scenario again, so this time we can listen to our intuition and let our conscience rule, rather than letting our emotions, or our ego, get the most of us.

Karma is recorded in the Akashic records, which can be accessed by some people through meditation. The Hall of the Akashic Records is similar to an Earth library, but it is not physical.

The Lords of Karma are in charge of all the Akashic Records. In this Hall there is an equivalent of a book that contains a record of everything our soul has experienced and the lives we have lived: a record of each life, all our accomplishments and unfinished life lessons, our spiritual growth, talents, and abilities built over all lifetimes, and a record of all our potentials to come.

We create bad karma by making imperfect decisions, which are usually the result of limited consciousness. Younger souls tend to create bad karma, and older souls tend to release it.

We can balance and release our karma by:

- Following our life purpose (more in Chapter 9).
- Taking responsibility, releasing blame, and letting go of drama. We make our lives more difficult when we keep blaming people and events for our circumstances (more in Chapter 13).
- Practicing forgiveness (more in Chapter 26).
- Consciously following the spiritual laws (explained throughout this book).
- Seeking to understand our life lessons and ensuring we learn from them.
- Making amends, as necessary, with whomever we feel we have "wronged." A genuine apology might be all that is needed. It is not required that the person consciously accepts it, he might

even be dead. If our soul feels genuinely remorseful, the action to make amends and try to rectify the problem proves that the lesson has been learned. Our soul knows not to do that again, and karma dissolves. We should always seek to rectify any wrongdoings, but we should not feel guilty for what we have or haven't done in the past. We can't balance karma by suffering; karma is not punishment.

Instant karma

The more evolved we are the quicker karma, both positive and negative, returns to us. This is called instant karma. Diana Cooper, in her book *A New Light on Ascension,* explains there are three exceptions to this:

1. We have past life contracts that attract low vibration people or circumstances. These contracts must be honored.
2. We have to face difficult situations or people in order to fulfill our chosen mission. This is why some great spiritual teachers seem to attract awful dramas, like Jesus Christ did.
3. We might be receiving tests of initiation by spiritual masters to strengthen weak areas. These might be presented to us as challenging relationships, financial situations, or difficulties at work.

Cooper's exceptions to the rule remind me of not being judgmental about people's misfortunes. Not every bad thing that happens to people is due to their "bad" karma. Some things are contracted prior to coming to Earth for a myriad of reasons that are not karma driven but serve the soul in some way. In other cases, it is just the result of poor understanding of the Laws of the Universe, in particular the Law of Attraction which we will discuss in the next Chapter.

7

The Law of Attraction

Nurture your mind with great thoughts,
for you will never go any higher than you think

BENJAMIN DISRAELI

THE CONCEPT THAT we create our own reality has been a staple of the New Age movement for a long time.

In Chapter 1, we saw that we are energy, and we emit or radiate a high or low vibration depending on our soul evolution and the quality of our thoughts and emotions, which get recorded and stay in the Field of Consciousness.

We create our own reality *partly* because of this; our thoughts and emotions build up our vibration, and that vibration is being answered by things that match it. We create constantly through our moment by moment thoughts and feelings, words, and actions. Everything in this universe is ultimately energy, and energy is influenced by our minds. Everything that exists around us, our home, car, and possessions was first created as a thought in somebody's mind. But there is something important to understand about creation; it does not come from this lifetime alone. We have seen in Chapter 4 how we create some of our required circumstances and agreements prior to coming to Earth. Also, sometimes karma has to be cleared before a new way can be manifested, or specific contracts must be honored.

We create our own reality, even if we don't understand so. For that reason, we often create by default. We create in two ways:

1. We create prior to incarnating per our life plan; for example, having a serious body ailment due to a genetic disease, being involved in an accident, or experiencing childhood traumas. We also create wonderful situations and synchronicities, including mentors and the knowledge to be able to deal with our life challenges.

2. We create consciously and unconsciously, with our thoughts and emotions, following the spiritual laws of the universe.

The Law of Attraction says that every thought, emotion, word, or action is on a vibrational frequency and radiates an energy that attracts people, events, and situations of the same waveband. Everything vibrates and everything emits a vibration. Therefore, the more balanced and in harmony we are, the more we will attract people and circumstances of the same vibration. The basic premise of this law is that like attracts like.

We manifest with our feelings, thoughts, and intentions, but our desires and beliefs need to be in synch; that is, we need to be in vibrational harmony with what we desire. For example, if you desire to be promoted but hold a belief that good things never happen to you, then it will be much harder for you to manifest it. Our life experiences are impacted by our thoughts about it, including the thought that we rarely get what we want. In this sense is where the Law of Attraction is significant: Our thoughts are shaping our reality.

Words are powerful too because they reinforce the energy of our feelings, but there is no point in pretending and saying that we are happy if we don't feel it. The Law of Attraction doesn't respond to our words; it will respond to the vibration that radiates from us.

It's becoming more common knowledge that we are, and become, what we think about, which is partly correct. But it is more accurate to say that we are the *feelings* we have when we think. So, if we say or think repeatedly, "I'm rich!" "I'm rich!" but feel poor, we will remain poor.

Do not fear the Law of Attraction. Just because we are not proficient at thinking positive thoughts it doesn't mean we are attracting all things negative; instant manifestation is not the norm.

In the spirit world thoughts create instantaneously. On Earth, because we were not yet masters of our own thoughts, it was necessary to introduce a time lag, an interval between the time a manifestation is set in motion and the time it is realized. Otherwise, if instant manifestation was the norm, it would not take long before we would manifest our greatest fears and die prematurely.

As our manifestation travels through this time lag, it will present itself only if we are at the vibration of the desire. Any time that we introduce attachment, fears, and impatience, we lower our vibration and the process needs to start all over again.

Thoughts don't have much energy in them. It is our emotions that amplify our thoughts and therefore our attraction: fear of doing things wrong, fear of the future, fear of not being good enough, or fear about attracting the wrong thing. Feeling prosperous and happy will attract abundance and situations that reflect them.

Emotion and passion will magnify our attraction.

How our thoughts impact everything around us

Masaru Emoto, in his book *The Hidden Messages in Water*, demonstrates how words and thoughts impact everything around us. He claimed that human consciousness has an effect on the molecular structure of water.

He discovered that crystals formed in frozen water reveal changes when specific, concentrated thoughts, are directed towards them.

Dr. Emoto visually captured the structure of water at the moment of freezing, and through high-speed photography he showed the direct consequences of destructive thoughts, as well as the thoughts of love and appreciation, in the formation of water crystals.

Loving thoughts created beautiful, precisely geometric crystals that looked like snowflakes. Hateful thoughts created horrible crystals, with chaotic and non-cohesive forms. Emoto found that the two words that created the most perfect pictures were love and gratitude.

We can extrapolate this experiment to look at the effect of how what we say to ourselves could impact our body. We are made up of about 60-70% water. What we think about all day long is literally shaping our physical bodies. Next time you look in the mirror and don't like what you see, try to be kind. Putting ourselves down can have bigger consequences than we ever thought possible.

Emoto also demonstrated the effect of positive and negative thinking on food. He placed portions of cooked rice in two containers and gave them to school children. On one container he wrote "Thank you," and on the other one he wrote, "You fool." He instructed the children to pass the rice around, and to say aloud what he had written on the labels in the jars, every day for 30 days ("Thank you," and "You fool"). After that period, the "Thank you" jar had barely changed, whereas the "You fool" jar was moldy and rotten.

I have read in many books the importance of blessing our foods before eating. This study certainly reminded me of that.

The role of gratitude

There is an inherent law of mind that we increase whatever we praise. The whole of creation responds to praise and is glad.

CHARLES FILLMORE

When we give thanks in advance for what we have asked for, we are recognizing and acknowledging that it is there. It is the ultimate faith that before we have asked, we have received an answer. The more grateful we are, the more we will receive things for which to be grateful for.

The Law of Attention says that whatever we put our attention on expands. It means that when we concentrate on the things we are grateful for in our lives, we will attract more of the same, and opportunities will increase to continue to enjoy the things we value. Appreciation is a state of mind that magnetizes money and abundance to us. It is all about our vibration; recognizing all that we already have puts us in a happy vibrational frequency of "more of this, please!".

The more time we spend in higher vibrations, the less time we will spend in limiting energies such as fear, anger, or the feeling that we are victims. The opposite is also true: If we give our attention to the things we dislike and the things we don't want, we will amplify and attract them to us.

You might find it a useful daily exercise to write five or ten things that you are grateful for. Sometimes it is not until we write it all down that we realize how fortunate we are.

Once you understand the Law of Attraction and apply it, you will find that life goes smoother, that you don't live in a chaotic, random world, and that you can master your own destiny.

8

Spiritual Laws of Creation

*I have established Laws in the universe that make it possible
for you to have – to create – exactly what you choose. These laws
can't be violated, nor can they be ignored. You cannot not
follow the Law for these are the ways things work.*

NEALE DONALD WALSCH,
FROM *CONVERSATIONS WITH GOD*

WE HAVE ALREADY discussed the impact of the Law of
Karma and the Law of Attraction in understanding our life
experiences and creation. In this chapter we are going to
learn how other spiritual laws can help us manifest everything we want
on Earth. They are the Law of Intention, the Law of Request, and the
Laws of Faith and Attachment.

With the term *creation* I mean creating abundance, joy, and
happiness in every aspect of our lives: finding our purpose, creating
the end of a difficult situation, getting a loan, going to college, or
improving our self esteem.

To create successfully we need to follow some rules:

- We must ask for the highest good for ourselves and everybody involved. Our creation must not harm somebody else, animals, or the earth.

- We should not aim to create a change in our spouse or for somebody to like us. When we do our inner work, everything outside of us changes too. Jim Rohn, described as a legend in the fields of motivation and personal achievement, said that we can change all things for the better when we change ourselves for the better. That includes all our relationships.

- We need to cooperate with others, not compete. If you are praying for a promotion and it goes to somebody else, know that it was not meant to be for you. Accept that graciously, even when you feel the chosen candidate is less qualified, or the process was unfair. Nobody else can fulfill your purpose, so believe that the best is yet to come. You cannot see the higher picture, so have faith and persevere in following your dreams. There any many ways to get to your destination; don't get hung up with what you perceive to be the one and only way.

- We must not take from somebody else in order to have abundance.

- We have to follow spiritual and man made laws. We cannot expect our business to thrive if we deceive our customers and/or the Internal Revenue Service (IRS). Don't waste your time, for example, trying to find ways to avoid your tax responsibilities when your time and energy could be spent in something productive, like meditating or making more sales calls. Nobody likes paying taxes, but If you are, it is because you are employed and earning money; the more taxes you are paying, the more money you are earning. Be grateful for all the abundance that comes your way instead, and see it grow beyond your dreams.

The Law of Intention

Intent is where manifestation begins. To start the process of creation we need to intend to have what we are asking for. That's because everything in the universe begins with intention, which triggers the transformation of energy. Clear intention equals clear results. (We need to intend to have a new car, not just merely wish or hope for one.)

When we intend to have something and we give our attention to it, we start activating that vibration within us. The more attention we give to any thought, the more dominant it becomes in our vibration.

Intention comes before thought. Our intent to create something would create itself into a thought of what we need to do to achieve it, and the manifestation process starts. Controlling our intentions is important because we move in the direction of our dominant thoughts.

We saw earlier that by paying constant attention to our unwanted things – I don't want to be fat, poor, or unhealthy – and by constantly thinking about them, we keep them stuck in our vibration, and we can't have a vibration of lack with a vibration of prosperity at the same time. We have to raise our vibration to match our desires by intending to do so. Intention is the first step.

Intent is one of the most powerful tools we have. It has been proven that we imprint the Field of Consciousness more strongly with our intent than with our actions. For example, closing our eyes and intending to stare at somebody will get a person to turn around faster than actually having our eyes opened and staring at him.

We also saw in Chapter 6 that intention is how karma is assessed. Our intent can be much more powerful than our actions.

The Law of Request

The Law of Request states that we need to ask for whatever we want. This usually applies to all situations. Unless we ask, we don't get. This is because we have been given free will, and not everybody who, for example, seems to be struggling actually wants or needs help.

If we want to draw assistance and knowledge from the Field of Consciousness, and/or our guides and angels, they need to know that we want help; otherwise, they can't intercede on our behalf. Nobody in the higher realms would ever interfere without a request. This has probably happened to you, you found yourself in a situation where you tried to help, but your unsolicited advice wasn't welcomed.

It doesn't matter in which situation we find ourselves, we can begin asking now. We don't have to wait for the perfect moment to start asking. There are many ways in which we can ask, but at the end of the day it doesn't matter how. What is important is that we do.

There is a big difference between requesting punctual help (for example, to give a great presentation at work, or to help you feel relaxed at the dentist) and requesting help for bigger life goals like finding your purpose, or improving your health, or your financial situation. For bigger goals, in conjunction with the methods explained in this chapter of prayer and writing letters, it is beneficial to create a document in which to set your goals. How to do this is explained in Chapter 10: The Power of Goal Setting.

These methods to request assistance are not mutually exclusive – you can write a letter, set goals, and pray.

Prayer

Prayer is the most common method to ask for what we want, out loud or silently. It doesn't have to be formal or follow a specific format. I usually talk a lot to my guides and angels in my head as I go along with my day.

A long time ago I read a fantastic book by Diana Cooper called *A Little Light on Angels,* which explained how willing and eager our angels are to help us with everyday tasks, or whatever else we need assistance with. That book has been updated and it is now called *New Light on*

Angels. You don't have to believe in angels for them to help you. You can call on them at any time.

Prayer causes us to focus, and by the Laws of Attraction and Attention, everything that is in vibrational harmony with our focus will come to us.

The Law of Attention says that whatever we are giving our attention to manifests in direct relation to the amount of attention we give it. If we focus on what we don't want, we will begin to notice it everywhere; if we focus on what we do want, that too will begin to become our reality.

You will notice that those who speak of prosperity, have it. Those who speak most of health, have it. Those who speak most of sickness, have it. Those who speak most of poverty, have it. It is Law.

THE TEACHINGS OF ABRAHAM®
(ESTHER AND JERRY HICKS BOOKS)

With our attention to any subject, the Law of Attraction delivers circumstances, conditions, experiences, other people, and all things that match our dominant vibration.

Write a letter

I like writing letters, usually addressed to one of the following, or all: God, the Universe, my guides, and angels. I like to write letters the old fashioned way with pen and paper because somehow, if I use my laptop, I feel detached from the content of the letter. Also, with pen and paper I seem to get more clarity in the process. In the same letter I put everything that is bothering me, and I don't do many letters per subject. I keep the letter in a drawer, and then I wait to receive guidance. Sometimes I do nothing else with it, yet at other times I might be guided to do something, such as to call a friend or relative or read a book.

The benefits of writing letters are twofold:

1. We might get clues and answers as we write; thoughts or pictures might come to our mind, which are already a partial or of full answer to our question or problem.
2. We will feel good knowing that we have started the process of doing something about our problems. After having the intent, asking is the second step to give permission to our guides and angels to help.

The difference between writing letters and setting goals is that when we write a letter we might write things down that we can't control. For example, if we are worried about a family member's upcoming operation, we might ask for help for them. We might also ask that our children be taken care of at school, or we might ask for things that eventually could end up in our goals plan (things we can control, like achieving a specific educational requirement, or manifesting a dream holiday).

Prayer and writing letters are ways to connect with our higher self, our guides, and angels. I also use meditation, which is explained in Chapter 19: Types of Conventional and Alternative Therapies. (Mind Therapies.)

At the same time, we can always ask people what we need to know. If you want a promotion, ask your boss what it takes to be promoted in your company. Bear in mind that anything you want to do in life has probably already been accomplished by somebody else, and I mean anything you have an interest in: writing and self-publishing a book, overcoming anxiety or health issues, starting a business, or raising a child. All these people have often documented the process to become successful, and it is likely that they have written a book about it, or they provide workshops, online courses, or seminars, or they can be contacted for mentoring. Go and find out how they did it.

The Law of Faith and Attachment

To receive what we want, we need to have the strength and courage to let it go. We need to release it with the full knowledge that it will return complete. This applies the final act that sets all manifestations fully into motion. It is the act of faith, which is closely linked to the Law of Attachment: if your sense of self-worth, status, or happiness is dependent on having something, then you are attached to it.

It is important to have faith and detachment because it is through our emotions, such as joy and happiness, that we attract what we want. Attachment is based on fear and insecurity, and those are low vibrating energies. If we attach ourselves to the lack of having something, then we will experience not having it.

In *The Law of Divine Compensation*, Marianne Williamson says that it is not our circumstances, but rather our thoughts about our circumstances, that determine our power to transform them. She explains that having faith in a positive outcome doesn't mean we are denying a problem or ignoring obstacles, it simply means we are affirming a solution.

Returning to the cake analogy, the way I see this law is this: if we want cake, we mix the ingredients, put it in the oven, and wait. We don't keep opening the oven to check that it is cooking; we need to have faith that the oven is taking care of it.

Take the first step in faith. You don't have
to see the whole staircase. Just take the first step.

MARTIN LUTHER KING, JR.

Trust divine timing

Sometimes we struggle to detach from our desired outcome because we become impatient. We wonder why we cannot manifest faster. There is a Chinese proverb that says there is no point pushing the river. The same applies with divine timing; sometimes things will take their own speed to manifest.

We saw in Chapter 7 how there is a time lag, an interval between the time a manifestation is set in motion and the time it is realized. As our manifestation travels through this time lag, it will only present itself if we are at the vibration of the desire. Also, sometimes the answer is no, or not now, or not in the requested form.

In the end, the speed of our manifestation is going to depend on some variables, but primarily upon these factors:

1. Manifestation done with passion and faith will manifest more quickly.
2. Our own *belief* system. If we believe "things take time," then they will take time. Or if we are not ready to receive it, it will be delayed accordingly.

We would not have a dream to be a photographer, a musician, or a stay at home mom if we had not set it all out before we came to Earth. We knew our higher self would be nagging us to fulfill what we planned to be, do, or have. Believe in yourself and know that you want to be these things because you planned it; otherwise, you would not be interested.

We need to believe that it is possible to have what we are asking for and hold that vision in front of us. We have to have faith. Beliefs create an energy that vibrates around us. Therefore, what we believe, we attract, and create.

Prosperity and success follow when we believe in ourselves.

9

Finding Your Purpose

As you follow the spiritual laws and raise your game, your mission here is revealed to you. When you have a vision of what you intend to accomplish during your journey on Earth, your clarity and purpose fill you with joy

DIANA COOPER, *A LITTLE LIGHT
ON THE SPIRITUAL LAWS*

THE LAW OF Dharma, or purpose in life, says that we have come to Earth to fulfill a purpose. We all have a unique talent and a reason for being here. Finding and creating our life purpose will bring the highest amount of abundance we have ever dreamed of.

Our higher self already knows what our purpose is, and knows the appropriate actions, thoughts, and synchronistic events that are right for us. Our higher self is constantly sending us impulses to move toward them, via our emotions. When we move in the right direction, our higher self is sending us feelings of excitement and joy. This is what it means to follow our intuition, and it's the reason so many books say that to find our purpose we need to follow our bliss or heart – it is because our soul's wisdom (our higher self) knows its way. Our higher self knows what is in our heart, our mind, and our vibration at any point in time; it knows how close or how far we are, vibrationally, from all things.

Our success will be directly proportional to the amount of joy and passion we experience on a daily basis. We need to do what we feel inspired to do, whatever motivates us. People who experience the highest amount of job satisfaction are those who approach their work as a calling; they don't work merely for the money or status.

Finding your purpose is paramount to your happiness on Earth. Many people feel lost and unhappy because they don't know what their purpose is, or they know what it is but they don't know how to manifest it.

If you don't know what your purpose is, you should make a conscious decision to find it. It is important for you to be able to live fully and purposely.

In *Silence: The Power of Quiet in a World Full of Noise,* Thich Nhat Hanh writes:

> If we don't have any purpose feeding us, we are just drifting. There are certain people whom I see only once a year. When I ask them what they have done in the past year, they can't remember. Sometimes, for most of us, days, whole weeks and even months go by like this, in a fog. This is because we're not aware of our intention on those days. Sometimes, it seems the only intention in us is just to make it through the day. We rarely offer ourselves the time and space to consider: Am I doing what I most want to be doing with my life? Do I even know what that is?

We don't need to make a living straight away with our passion; what is important is that we begin to move in the direction of it. Bear in mind that some things that brings us great joy may not necessarily have a direct correlation with our life's purpose, but these may be tasks that brings us closer to finding and achieving our purpose.

For example, you might love cooking because it puts you in the right mood and de-stresses you, and this state of relaxation provides you with ideas for the blog or book you are working on.

Don't underestimate how important it is to have "play time" in your life. Whether it is to cook, exercise, watch a movie, or take a bath – if it brings you joy it is because your higher self sees the task as a worthwhile endeavor, and is bringing forth the emotion of joy to help you recognize it as such.

Our life purpose doesn't have to be one thing

Our life purpose doesn't have to be one thing and the same thing throughout our lives. We can have multiple passions, and these passions can change depending on our soul evolution while on Earth as well as on our changing circumstances. We have free will, and so does everybody around us. We might have planned to be at some part of the world in our thirties, but for whatever reason we postpone the idea or we completely abandon it.

Don't worry about finding your purpose straight away or getting answers quickly. As we saw earlier, one single thing, like cooking, or taking a bath, might lead to many other things or ideas.

Sometimes our life purpose is to support another soul. We saw earlier in Chapter 4: Pre-Birth Planning Sessions that we choose to come to Earth for a variety of reasons. In the book *Journey of Souls*, Dr. Newton explains the story of a patient whose purpose for incarnating in a Canadian life was solely to be the caretaker of Billy, her bother. Dr. Newton's patient knew that Billy would be badly hurt (burnt) at age four, and she agreed to take care of him. Billy's major lesson for allowing his body to be hurt was to acquire humility without being crushed by a life of little self-gratification.

Timing

What can you do if you don't know what your purpose is?

There is a lot to be learned trying to find our way there. Sometimes in the planning sessions we don't set ourselves to find our purpose and fully work on it until we are forty, fifty, or older. That's because we might not be ready to fulfill it before that time.

So while you are in your twenties worrying that you don't know what to do, or that you have chosen the incorrect job, career, or college course, please know that you might be exactly where you need to be for that time in your life. Perhaps you decided to have children first, take care of them, and then pursue other interests. The most important thing is to listen to your higher self and follow the promptings it gives you to find the highest amount of joy at every moment. If what you're doing fills you with joy, then whatever you're doing is your purpose at that time.

When I was ready to go to University I had no idea what I wanted to do with my life. A lot of people in my class had no idea which way to go either, and we were all being told different things:

- "A bad course choice could ruin your life."
- "There are no good job opportunities for that type of course."
- "That type of career doesn't pay well."
- "Your mom or dad prefers if you become a ...."
- "You are too intelligent to choose to be a ...."
- "You should aim for this or that university, with this or that type of degree."

General claims about "best remunerated," "best job prospects," or "best social status" don't mean much. Our soul cares about us following our life plan, our dreams and passions, releasing and clearing our karma, and evolving in the process – not about ego driven attributes.

We cannot "ruin" our lives with a decision we made because we can always pick up from where we are, at any given moment. Actually, I can't think of any action that could make us ruin our lives. The fact that we are imperfect, and we make less than perfect decisions, is a given; we wouldn't be here if we were perfect. We are bound to make many mistakes and hopefully learn from them. We all create our future with our thoughts and actions in the now.

Please remember that sometimes our closest friends and family are just projecting their own experiences, fears, and limitations, and it has nothing to do with our ability to create the life we want. Despite our upbringing, circumstances, and financial background, we all have the same energy potential as everyone else.

Nido Qubein, businessman, motivational speaker, and author, says:

Your present circumstances don't determine where you can go, they merely determine where you start.

Divine timing might mean that your time is now, and not decades ago. Don't dwell on what you could have done and didn't, how you should have spent your money, or what you should or should not have studied. Do it now, or let it go, but let go of drama and move forward. Living in regret and guilt is one of the most wasteful and unproductive activities we can engage in.

* * *

Getting clarity will help you toward finding your purpose. You might be able to start by eliminating bothersome life issues that are clogging your ability to see what is in store for you.

Here are some questions to help you get clarity about what you want are:

1. What is bothering you the most at this moment in time? Is it your health, your job, lack of self esteem, or being lonely? Once you start dealing with these items, you might be able to concentrate on finding your purpose. Dealing with your

biggest issues will clear the path; otherwise, you will be too preoccupied with them.

2. What did you desire to be or do as a child? Children are closer to their soul energy and they don't question it, so our childhood dreams often provide us with the best clues. Did you enjoy dancing more than anything else? Even symbolic things might give you a clue. For example, if all you wanted to do was to climb mountains, you might thrive in an environmental job or as a forest ranger.

3. What would make you happy right now? What lifestyle change could you make to give you more happiness or peace of mind now? What changes do you need to make to achieve this?

4. What would you like to have more of or completely eliminate?

5. In the longer term, what's the one thing you would love to do before you die?

6. What would you do if you knew you couldn't fail?

Ultimately, setting your goals will help you gain clarity, to focus on what is important and what you want to achieve in your life. We will discuss goal setting in the next chapter.

The books on this topic that I recommend are:

- *The Success Principles: How to Get from Where You Are to Where You Want to Be,* by Jack Canfield and Janet Switzer
- *Creating Money: Attracting Abundance,* by Sanaya Roman

Death is not the greatest loss in life.
The greatest loss is what dies inside us while we live

NORMAN COUSINS

10

The Power of Goal Setting

If you don't have direction it doesn't matter which road you take

AUTHOR UNKNOWN
(ATTRIBUTED TO VARIOUS PEOPLE)

THE IMPORTANCE OF setting goals has been researched for decades. Many studies have shown that people who write down their goals and commit to them are much more likely to achieve them. There is a big difference between wanting to be rich and deliberately creating a path to achieve it.

Goal setting is nothing more than a list of all the things you wish to achieve, with a deadline and an action plan to achieve them. It can be as detailed as you wish. Your goals could be anything from learning more about a subject to figuring out what your purpose is, making more friends, opening a store, or getting a new car.

Before you start a goal setting plan, honestly assess where you are now. It will help you prioritize and narrow down what you want or need to accomplish first. Your goals must answer your most fundamental needs: What do you want to be, do, or have? Usually, it is the things you haven't done that will generate your biggest regret.

Goal setting guidelines

The way to get started is to quit talking and start doing

WALT DISNEY

1. First and foremost, make sure you understand what is bothering you and what your life priorities are. Take care of those first; otherwise, you might end up totally scattered, stressed out, and with too much on your plate. Trying to open a new business might be a good idea, but probably not while you are recovering from your health issues or handling your divorce at the same time.

2. There is something very important to understand before you set any goals: whatever you want to achieve, it has to bring you joy in the *process* of achieving it. This is because:
   o If there is no joy, there is no point. We came to Earth to enjoy life, not to struggle. It doesn't mean it won't involve hard work, but it should be joyful.
   o Once you achieve your goals, it will also take effort and actions to maintain the status quo. For example, if your goal is to lose a specific amount of weight, or if you work hard to win an audition, there will be a lot of hard work involved after you achieve those goals; namely, to keep the weight off, or to be the best actor, singer, or whatever you auditioned for (you will have to keep training). Every goal achieved brings a new set of responsibilities.

I once saw an interview with French actress Marion Cotillard. She was talking about one of her films, *La Vie en Rose*. Her performance won her a Golden Globe and an Oscar for playing the character of Edith Piaf, a singer. What struck me the most from her interview was her determination to be an outstanding actress. The interviewer asked her why, knowing that she would be lip syncing, she had decided to take singing lessons. She replied that in order to do her best she wanted to know where to position her tongue, how to move her mouth, and how to stand while singing. I'm not an actress, but if somebody told me that I would be lip syncing I don't think it would have occurred to me to take singing lessons.

That interview reminded me that as important as it is to achieve our goals (win the part), it is at least as important to do our best after achieving them. Achieving a goal is not always our ultimate destination.

3. Be very clear about what you want

If you don't have clarity about what you want, you can't expect to receive it. Clarity is essential.

A way to assist you with the process of getting clarity is to split your desires and dreams into different categories (additionally, you may also use some of the questions to find clarity about our life purpose that we learned about in the previous chapter). Below are some examples; please add a category, such as travel or love, if it is important for you:

- Career: What would you like to accomplish this year? How much would you like to earn?
- Family: Do you want to spend more time with your kids or partner, or improve your relationship with them?
- Personal growth: Would you like to read more books, attend workshops, or learn to be more confident or assertive?
- Health: How could you get more energy in your life? Time for sleep, relaxation, and meditation would fall in this category.
- Pleasure: How can you have more fun?
- Friends and community, service to others: How can you help others? Charity work and contributions are two ideas that fit here.

4. Once you are clear about what you want, make sure to ask for the essence of it.

Most of us want things because we believe that having them will make us feel good. That is really the bottom line, but for the most part that happiness is short-lived and we are on to the next thing. This happens because we haven't asked for the essence of what we want. The essence is the higher quality that the item will fulfill. What function is it going to perform, and what do we need it for? When we are in touch with the essence of what we desire, we can have it in many ways.

For example, say you work a late or night shift, and you have become increasingly concerned about your safety walking to the bus stop at night in order to get home. You might think that the answer would be for you to own a car, so you decide that you are going to find the money to buy one. However, the essence of what you are really looking for is to feel safe and secure getting home from work. You might buy a car only to find that the one you were able to afford has too many maintenance issues and is adding a lot of stress to your already stressed life, or you buy a brand new one but you can't keep up with the monthly payments. What you need to ask for is for a way to arrive safely at your home after work, for that is what you really want.

Then you might find that numerous solutions appear. You might find that you are able to apply for the same position during the day when you can take the bus safely, or that there is a co-worker who works the same shifts and is willing to give you a lift in exchange for some gas money. Or you might even find a job closer to your home. (And, of course, getting a car might be a potential answer too.)

Asking for the essence of what you want, and asking for something specific, are not mutually exclusive. You might feel you need a break from work to get some peace and rest, which is the essence, and at the same time you want to go to Hawaii. You may use the same goal for that purpose.

5. Break down your goals into smaller, actionable steps, and then continue breaking down those steps until you have a plan for

all your goals. Your goals and sub goals need to be manageable. You need to be very clear about how you will know if you have accomplished them.

Your dream or goal might be to return to college, but you need to break it down further:

- What type of courses do you want to take?
- Which colleges offer those courses (and is it part time, full time, online)? Have you looked thoroughly at all the available options?
- What funds do you need, and what are the pre-entry requirements?
- If you have children under your care, who is going to look after them?
- How will you find the time to study once you enroll?

The reason to do this is to focus and work your way through any potential issues, and to set smaller goals that are achievable so you have a step by step plan that you can follow.

You might want to ask for money, in general, and there is nothing wrong with that. However, the more clarity you have around what you need and what it looks like, the easier it will be to plan and manifest it. Instead of asking "I want a million dollars," (and I will think what to do with it later), you may want to write instead, "I want to pay off the mortgage."

When breaking down your goals delegate as many tasks as you can. Take an honest look at how you spend your money and, when possible, rearrange expenditures so you are moving toward achieving your goals. If you find that you spend a lot of money eating out or drinking, you might want to use that money to pay for a cleaner, or a gardener, or some other type of helper who frees your time to do what is important to you, such as, spending time with your kids, making more sales calls, reading a motivational book, or taking a course. It doesn't mean you are never going to eat out again; it just means that you are using your money to your best advantage to move in the direction of your goals. When possible, it is important to delegate all the routine duties that don't add value to your goals. Writing your goals down allows you to take a closer look at what you really want, and most importantly, why.

Don't be put off by goals that might take long to achieve, like learning to play a new instrument or going back to college. If your soul has been nagging you to do it for a long time, try to find a way to do it. One of my favorite quotes is from Earl Nightingale:

> *Never give up on a dream just because of the time it will take to accomplish it. The time will pass anyway.*

6. Be honest. Your goals are just for you and nobody else. What do you really want? You might think you want to lose weight or to have an expensive car, but in reality you just want fewer (or more) working hours and to make amends with a friend.

7. Set goals that you can control. For example: "I will open up a restaurant when the economy improves" is too vague, and there is nothing you can do about the economy. Set goals that totally depend on you to achieve them. The goal might still be "I want to open a restaurant," but you can then have many sub-goals that you can control: (a) Do market research to decide best area and viability, (b) Save money or make a business plan to obtain finances, etc.

8. Make your goals measurable. You have probably read that what you measure is what you get. If the essence or goal is "to improve my relationship with my children," you can break it down further as follows:
   - Go to the movies with my children once a month.
   - Make time to sit down for breakfast or dinner with my children, with all electronics, phones, and TV turned off, at least three or five times a week.

- Have one-to-one chats with my children every couple of weeks.
- Make time to attend their weekend games.

9. Aim high. I mentioned earlier that it is important to set very specific goals. However, the only caveat with being very specific is that we are limiting the possibilities of what is energetically available to us. For this reason, it is good practice to picture something higher than the best outcome we can imagine. Someone once said, *"If people are not laughing at your goals, your goals are too small."* This is because we have a tendency to underestimate ourselves. Top athletes, rich entrepreneurs, and very high achievers understand that in order to achieve success they need to set goals beyond their best results.
Once you have written your goal, ask yourself: Is this the best outcome that could happen?

10. Prioritize. Now that you understand which goals are relevant, make sure to prioritize them. Confusion is solved by getting your priorities straight. Decide what you need to do now and what you can do later.

Priority might mean different things to different people. Think about what is important for you, and what is bothering you the most at the moment. Would you feel much better in the short term if you finally took the much needed week off to clear your head and sleep? There is no right or wrong answer, but to start with you will benefit from tackling those items that will bring you the most satisfaction and fulfillment in the short term, particularly if they have been bothering you for a long time.

Try not to overload yourself with multiple "nice to have" goals. You are not racing against anybody. If you are overwhelmed with tasks and priorities cut them down to a reasonable size and learn about time management. A great book that can help you with this is *15 Secrets Successful People Know About Time Management*, by Kevin Kruse.

11. Attach a timeline to all your goals. Write the goal and decide when you are going to accomplish it by. Have deadlines and sub deadlines as necessary, or an ongoing deadline (going once a month to the cinema with your kids can be a recurrent monthly goal).

12. Follow the path of least resistance. Sometimes things are not difficult; we make them difficult. When you are going after a specific goal and you find too many doors closing, so it is very difficult to get there, make sure to notice that. There is a difference between persevering to achieve a goal, and going down the wrong path to get it. Be flexible with your choices and listen to your intuition.

13. Sign and date your list. It will give it power. Write down something uplifting and read it to yourself often: "This or something better manifests for me now. My dreams come true! I'm unstoppable!"
And commit to it!

*I can accept failure; everyone fails at something.
But I can't accept not trying.*

MICHAEL JORDAN

11

The Power of Your Mind to Create

*The Buddhist meditation masters know how flexible and
workable the mind is. If we train it, anything is possible*

SOGYAL RINPOCHE

AUSTRIAN PSYCHOLOGIST SIGMUND Freud (1856-1939) was the first known person to introduce the idea that the human mind is contained in three levels of awareness, or consciousness. He termed them the conscious, preconscious (in some literature is called subconscious), and unconscious.

According to this model, *the conscious mind* is the rational decision maker, and it defines all thoughts and actions within our awareness. It is our ego personality and its belief system. People who don't believe in having a soul, or spiritual self, usually think they are just their ego.

The subconscious mind defines all reactions and automatic actions, and it can't reason like our conscious mind does.

Have you ever over-reacted to a minor incident? What's really happening is that the same type of unwanted behavior, or situation, has happened enough times to be permanently sealed in your subconscious mind, which is a million times more powerful than your conscious mind, and one more occurrence of the same issue pushes you over the top.

The unconscious mind is the soul presence. Often called higher self (or inner self), it has full knowledge of our planning sessions, contracts and agreements, and all past events and memories which are usually (consciously) inaccessible to us. It is the bridge between the soul and the Earth plane. It is the part that is accessed through kinesiology and tapping; it is the seat of our intuition.

The conscious and subconscious minds are interdependent. With the conscious mind we will conjure up all our positive thoughts, but it is with repetition that those will be ingrained in the subconscious mind. We can use the power of our mind to learn new habits because our subconscious mind learns from patterns and the repetition of patterns.

The subconscious mind runs all the programs of automatic behavior. We learn how to drive, and then one day without our conscious effort we arrive at our destination. It has probably happened to you: You get in your car, you start driving, and then you take the road to work although you didn't mean to go that way and it was your day off. This is important to understand because with the power of our subconscious mind we can create new habits that will serve us in achieving our goals.

The subconscious mind controls all the vital processes of our body, and our unconscious (or higher self), knows the answers to our problems.

The periods when we are drifting off to sleep and upon awakening are two of the most significant doorways into the sub-conscious. Particularly at night we can ask our subconscious mind what we need to know, or how to resolve an issue, and our sub-conscious mind will work on our goals or any tasks that we give it all night long. We might also want to visualize the day ahead; waking up feeling energized and in an excellent mood, our morning meetings going very well, and accomplishing whatever is important for us.

By accessing that deeper mind, we can rewrite those issues and habits. We can do that in various ways: with affirmations, visualizations, visual boards, and meditation. In addition to that, I also recommend you read *The Power of Your Subconscious Mind: Riches Are Within Your Reach*, by Paul Joseph Murphy.

Affirmations

A lot has been said about the effectiveness, or lack thereof, of affirmations. Some people say they don't work, yet others that they absolutely do. From my point of view, their efficacy depends on how we are wording the affirmation, how we *feel* while affirming it, and whether we are taking any action to accomplish what we want.

Were you told as a child that you were useless, and you believed it? Were you bullied into thinking that you were too fat, or ugly, to be liked? It didn't matter that it was untrue; you still believed it, because we come to believe whatever we are repeatedly told, or whatever we repeat to ourselves. To affirm is to make firm, to manifest our thoughts in material form.

Our subconscious mind learns through strong emotion and repetition. It doesn't know what is real or fantasy– and it takes everything personally. When we see a sad film, although we know it is not real, our subconscious mind doesn't know the difference and we cry. When we are gossiping, judging, or cursing people, our subconscious is registering a feeling of inadequacy and disdain, but it is unable to determine whether we are upset with somebody else or with ourselves.

Affirmations are a powerful tool for reprogramming the subconscious mind because the subconscious mind doesn't create new ideas; it just accepts as true those that the conscious mind thinks are true.

The Law of Affirmation says that we bring about what we affirm. This law is closely connected to the Law of Attraction. If we constantly affirm that we are useless we will attract to ourselves situations that reinforce our belief that we are useless.

Keys to successful affirmations

1. Make your affirmations possible, uplifting, firm, and unwavering. You need to affirm that which you resonate with, because affirmations carry their own vibration. "I manifest a million dollars in the near future" might not feel doable or achievable (particularly if you have been struggling financially for a long time). You might choose instead, "everything always works out for me."

2. Repeat. There is a lot of power in repetition. You will be reprogramming your subconscious mind to accept what you affirm as the new reality, and it will create circumstances to bring about what you now believe.

3. Be positive, short, and use I AM phrases as much as possible. "I am" is the strongest creative statement in the universe. Instead of saying "I am debt free" (your subconscious mind reads "debt"), try instead "I am wealthy beyond measure."

Our subconscious mind doesn't compute negatives. It is like a computer that can't take negative commands. When you are told, "don't think of an elephant," the first image that comes to mind is... an elephant.

We can't desire something, focus on the absence of it, and expect to receive it. An example of a negative affirmation is "I don't want to be broke," or "I am not poor anymore."

Even on normal day to day situations, instead of saying "Don't forget to do your homework," it is best to say, "Remember to do your homework," or "Stay on the pavement," instead of "Don't cross the road."

4. Tie your affirmations to the goals you wrote earlier. Make them significant for you.

Self-fulfilling prophecy

Watch the power of your words, for you will believe and execute what you repeatedly tell yourself. "I'm always late." "It is difficult to make new friends." "I always catch a cold in the winter."

Affirmations can be very powerful tools for manifestation, but you need to use them the right way. At the same time, they are not imperative for success. I'm sure there are a lot of wealthy and successful people who have never used an affirmation in their lives (or at least not consciously). Many paths arrive at the same destination. Use your intuition and discernment to decide what works for you.

An excellent book with many affirmations is *The Wealthy Spirit: Daily Affirmations for Financial Stress Reduction*, by Chellie Campbell. Each chapter of this book contains an uplifting quote, a brief story relative to the chapter's title, and a closing affirmation for a total of 365 affirmations. That's a lot of affirmations to learn from. A great read.

Visualizations

*If you do not see great riches with your imagination,
you will never see them in your bank balance.*

NAPOLEON HILL, FROM *THINK AND GROW RICH*

Visualization, through the Law of Attraction, magnetizes and attracts to you the people, resources, and opportunities you need to achieve your goals.

Visualization works for the same reason affirmations do: Our subconscious mind has no idea what is real or what is not. It only knows what the conscious mind tells it, so by placing positive and uplifting pictures in our mind, repeatedly, our subconscious mind activates them as real.

The universe doesn't know if our vibration is because we are experiencing something real, or because we are imagining it. In either case, it answers the vibration, and by the Law of Attraction the manifestation must follow.

Visualizations need to be done with great emotion. Emotions energize our thoughts and propel them to the outer world. That which we feel strongly, we will experience. The stronger our emotions are, the more rapidly we create what we are thinking about. By making our positive thoughts more vivid and real, we increase our ability to create what we want.

Another reason why we need to visualize adding strong emotion is that we always remember events by their emotion attached to them. The stronger the emotion felt (good or bad), the more we remember it. When we visualize our dreams coming true, the feeling of excitement and magnetism is more important than any other step.

Visualization is a well-known tool used by top athletes. In 2014, when the Winter Olympics were held in Sochi, Russia, *The Huffington Post* featured an article[7] called *The brain training secrets of Olympic athletes.* The article discussed the importance of the mind and visualizations for Olympians.

> "The physical aspect of the sport can only take you so far," said Olympic gold medal-winning gymnast Shannon Miller during an interview with the Dana Foundation. "The mental aspect has to kick in, especially when you're talking about the best of the best. In the Olympic games, everyone is talented. Everyone trains hard. Everyone does the work. What separates the gold medalists from the silver medalists is simply the mental game."

A classic book to help you understand the process of visualization and how to do it is *Creative Visualization,* by Shakti Gawain.

---

[7] http://www.huffingtonpost.com/2014/02/11/mind-hacks-from-olympic-a_n_4747755.html

Vision board

A vision board is a poster on which you create a collage of images you have collected from various places. The images you put on a vision board relate to your desires: a picture of a new car, receiving a trophy, a happy family life, or a holiday destination.

Vision boards work because symbols are very powerful. They bypass all our thoughts and beliefs regarding what we think it is possible for us to have. When we have faith in a vision it must succeed. For that reason, we need to use images that are inspiring and make us feel good. You can use a mix of magazine images, angel or tarot cards with nice images or phrases, Internet images (you can Google the image you are looking for, or you can buy it), and your own photos.

A vision board combines images with words and/or affirmations. Not everybody puts words on their board. I like putting a mission statement on top of the board that says what I'm trying to accomplish (my intent). I also write words that have a meaning for me; for example, "In the next three months" or "Thank you." My preference is to have a neat and tidy board where I can clearly see the pictures and it feels right. I don't like many superimposed pictures on top of each other, but you need to do what feels right for you.

You can use one theme for the board; for example, it can be all about your career, or you can use many themes, like putting a picture of the house of your dreams and a desired vacation destination.

Once you have your vision board, look at it daily, even for a few moments. Energize it by saying thank you, feeling grateful and positive for what is to come. Imagine you already have it and jump for joy. The better you feel doing this exercise, the quicker you will bring about what you want.

You can find a lot of free content and explanations on how to make a vision board at *Make a Vision Board* webpage.[8] I also recommend Christine Kane's book, *The Complete Guide to Vision Boards.*

---

[8] http://makeavisionboard.com/

Meditation

Meditation is a wonderful tool to still our minds and relax, and it is another way to raise our vibration to match our desires. Meditation is explained further in Chapter 19: Types of Conventional and Alternative Therapies. (Mind therapies.)

◆ ◆ ◆

Everything we have learned so far in this book to help us manifest our purpose and achieve our goals is very important, but it is equally important to take action.

12

Take Action

*You are never given a wish without also being given the power
to make it come true. You may also have to work for it, however*

RICHARD BACH

THE SAYING, "LET go and let God" is often misunderstood.
Whoever originally coined that phrase was probably thinking
about the Law of Attachment: if your happiness or sense of
self-worth is dependent on having something, then you are attached to
it. But "Let go and let God" does not refer to doing nothing.
Rabindranath Tagore, 1913 Nobel Prize Winner in Literature, said that
we can't cross the sea merely by staring at the water.

We should not ask for what we want and wait for "the universe"
to provide it. There is no point finding your purpose, drafting your
goals, prioritizing them, setting deadlines, following the spiritual laws
and using the power of your mind to manifest if in the end you don't
take action.

We need to purposely go after what we want. It is true that in
some cases the action might be to do nothing at all, like waiting for the
cake to bake, but in most cases we are going to be guided to do

something: turn the oven up or down, update our resume, take a class, go to the post office, take a bath, revisit our goals, call a friend, etc. Once we have completed that step, we will be guided to take the next step, and the next, until we reach our goal.

Once we feel we have taken all possible action, then we let go and let God. If you find that you are struggling to understand what your next step should be, it is because you haven't formed a clear picture of what you want, and therefore your higher self can't bring it to you. Clarity is essential.

Your actions should be in line with all the steps and mini goals in your life, or goal plan. The universe won't do the physical work for you, although it is true that God, your guides, and angels will certainly guide you to your next steps. It is useful to use all the tools provided in the previous chapters, but at some point you have to take action and move in the direction of your dreams.

Take action on the fact that you expect your life to change!

Use your intuition

If you do not get it from yourself, where will you go for it?

BUDDHA

The Law of Discrimination says that we have intuition that can guide us to make the best choices for our highest good. When we put a request out, our higher self tries to bring it to us. We have already seen that the way it talks to us is via our intuition, or inner guidance. Both positive and warning signals are usually felt via our emotions, like a gut feeling urging us to do something, or not to go somewhere. In contrast, the urge to pick up the phone to call somebody might be a sudden thought about that person.

If we ask our intuition a question, we will receive the answer in many ways:

- Primarily, via our emotions. This can be a hunch to go somewhere, to do or not do a specific task. Our gut instinct is usually all we need.
- Through visual images in our mind.
- Through sound, like when getting in the car and suddenly hearing a song with specific meaningful lyrics.
- Our guides and angels might also assist to provide an answer, bringing people and situations to our life through synchronistic events. Being "in the right place at the right time" is not coincidence.

Our intuition will never guide us to do crazy things, so try not to use logic on your intuition. If you are asking how to get a pay raise, and you receive a feeling or a thought to go to your local book store, or an image of your local library, don't block it off thinking it has nothing to do with it, or that your intuition doesn't work. You might find a book about crucial conversations that gives you just the right tips for approaching your manager. Or it might be that they have a job posting advertised that you are really interested in (and the pay raise you are asking for doesn't come from your current job). I have said it before, but trust your higher self; it knows what you need to succeed and where to find it.

Review your progress and goals

Every time we review our goals we put our attention on them. We saw earlier that, by the Law of Attention, whatever we give our attention to manifests in direct relation to the amount of attention we give it.

We know that when we put our attention on the negative aspects of our life, we don't improve them; however, a positive outlook typically provides a wider set of answers to the same problem.

Pay attention to your goals, review them often, and decide where to spend your time. A way to focus on your key goals is to reduce them to only a few, or just one goal, until you achieve that one and you are ready to move on to the next one. A great book about concentrating on one item and understanding what is your one priority is *The One Thing: The Surprising Simple Truth Behind Extraordinary Results*, by Gary Keller and Jay Papasan.

Did you find you were too optimistic, and now you haven't accomplished half of what you intended to do? Block time each week to review your monthly and annual goals. It is okay if you decide you don't want to pursue a goal any longer. It doesn't matter if you scrap the whole list. The most important thing is to be happy with the progress you are making. It might be that you are doing so much inner work that the list of things you originally thought were important aren't anymore.

It is only you who needs to keep track of that list. Goals are there to help you become who you want to be. Change the deadline, or choose not to pursue them any longer. Also remember, "Life happens." For example, you get married or you split up with your boyfriend, you change jobs or you lose your job. Some life events will prevent you, or make it difficult for you to commit to a goal, and that's okay. You aren't racing against anybody. Sometimes you will make mistakes too. We all do. Change course or remove a goal. Do what you need to do and move forward.

Persevere

It always seems impossible until it is done

NELSON MANDELA

How motivated are you to accomplish your goals? We don't usually fail because of our lack of capability; we fail because we don't persevere enough to see it done.

Put your whole heart into making your dreams come true. Successful people persevere, and they don't take no for an answer. They keep going until they get what they want. If one way didn't work, they try another. They keep reaching for the goal. They don't give up.

Jack Canfield, co-author of *The Chicken Soup for the Soul®* books, success coach, and author of many books including the co-authored (with Janet Switzer) best seller, *Success Principles: How to Get from Where You Are to Where You Want to Be,* writes that whenever we ask anyone for anything, remember the following:

SWSWSWSW
Which stands for *Some Will, Some Won't; So What - Someone's Waiting*!

Not everybody is going to say yes, so just keep going until you find the person who does. The first *Chicken Soup for the Soul®* book was rejected by publishers 144 times, but the Chicken Soup for the Soul series has since gone on to sell over 500 million copies. Can you imagine if the authors had just given up?

Canfield offers personal coaching, success products, and numerous workshops.[9] I have attended one of these workshops; it was called "One Day to Greatness," and it was fantastic. I also highly recommend his co-authored (with Janet Switzer) book *Success Principles: How to Get from Where You Are to Where You Want to Be.*

You have probably heard of many instances where people achieved great things through persistence. Alan Cohen, in his book *I Had It All the Time: When Self Improvement Gives Way to Ecstasy,* writes that your package might be delivered by another carrier. I like that analogy. He gives the example of The Beatles, who were turned down by ten recording companies before Capitol Records took them on.

Every time you are rejected, remember Canfield words: So what? Someone is waiting!

---

[9] http://jackcanfield.com/training-events/

13

Take Responsibility

*If you could kick the person in the pants responsible for
most of your trouble, you wouldn't sit for a month*

THEODORE ROOSEVELT

IF WE WISH to be happy and successful, we must accept more
personal responsibility for our own happiness. We are not at the
mercy of unknown powers; once we realize we are responsible for
our thoughts, feelings, and experiences, we achieve freedom. It doesn't
mean that we accept or agree with what is happening, but we
understand that within us we have the power to choose peace. How
many times have you said, "I'm not going to let that get to me?" You
can always choose to walk away, have a better reaction, or have a
better thought.

One of the biggest stresses in life is when we feel we have no
control over a situation; however, without responsibility there is no
power. When we take responsibility we are able to resolve our
problems and work through our karma.

To take responsibility means to take back your power, let go of
blame, and let go of drama.

Take back your power

We tend to give our power away when we continue to blame our parents, partners, and friends for our circumstances or how they make us feel. We also give our power away to outside authorities who claim to know the truth and want the best for us; for example, this happens in medicine, in politics, with dieting companies, and in the entertainment industry.

We should use our discernment in everything. Just because "everybody" seems to be raving about a product or service doesn't mean it will be right for us.

How we give our power away:

- We give our power away to the past, our childhood, and our upbringing. I know it's hard to overcome a difficult childhood, but it does serve us well to concentrate now on what we can do to feel better, and how to move forward and upward with our life.

- We compare ourselves to other people to decide if we are talented, beautiful, or smart enough.

- In politics, we are led to believe that one person or another will fix our problems, or make our country a better place, but a perfect politician or government is not essential to our experience of wealth, happiness, and well-being. I fully understand that it is easier to live under some political regimes than others, but politicians can't choose our state of mind. They can't choose our thoughts, or if we let things get to us or not. They can't choose with whom we hang out, or how much or how little we exercise. And they can't stop us from writing our goals, standing up for ourselves, or doing our inner work. Only we have the power to help ourselves.

- We give our power away when we let people "walk over us" while we're trying to please them. If you struggle with saying no, you might benefit from going to an assertiveness training course, or reading a book on the subject.

You have the right to refuse a request from people without feeling selfish or guilty. Are you asked too often to cook at family gatherings, or are you asked to babysit your friend's or family's kids too often and you don't know how to refuse? You don't have to explain why you are busy, but if you are like me, who feels you have to provide explanations, you might just want to say, "Sorry, I have a full plate." I think we all want to feel wanted and liked, but if you feel you are being taken advantage of it will serve you well to put your foot down. There is nothing you can do about people who choose to be upset when you say "no." True friends and people who care for you will say, "I'm sorry you have a full plate. Can I help?" The more you stand up for yourself, the more respect you will earn, which in turn will attract people who are respectful of you and your time.

In the book, *Living with Joy*, Sanaya Roman explains:

> *Do not wait for other people to respect you or treat you in a more positive way. They will not until you treat yourself with respect.... You do not need to get angry or demand your rights, for that only creates a power struggle between you and the others. No matter how good you feel about yourself, there will always be those who do not treat you in a respectful way, for they have not learned to treat themselves in a loving way. The relationships you have with others can only be as good as the relationship you have with yourself.*

- We give our power away when we don't attempt to resolve a problem unless we have sought the opinion of a trusted friend, parent, or guru. We accept their opinion as truth, and we take action based on what they say, even if their advice goes against our intuition.

Clearly, sometimes it is wise and appropriate to seek advice from other people, but do so with the intent to combine the information they give you with your own inner knowing.

There is a quote attributed to Zen Master Linji that says, "If you meet the Buddha, kill him." It is not a literal statement; it basically means that if you find anybody who claims that he has all the truth, and that you should follow him, you should run away fast because true wisdom lies inside you. A true spiritual teacher will tell you that he or she is not teaching you, but reminding you of what you already know, because in truth, your soul knew all of this before you came here.

- We give our power away to lucky charms, superstitions, and the like. A lucky ornament, necklace, or charm is going to bring us luck to the extent that we *believe* it to do so.

- We give away our power when we convince ourselves that we can't live without a thing, a pet, or a person.

- We give our power away when we run away from our problems; for example, moving out of the area we live in, changing jobs, or leaving our partner. The problem is that wherever we go, if we haven't changed our vibrational stance, nothing will change. We will think and act the same way as before, and therefore we will attract the same experiences.
If we haven't done the inner work required, a new city or job will not bring us what we need. The change has to happen within. When there is peace and joy in our heart, the things and people we meet will give us peace and joy.

Let go of blame

"I didn't get to the interview on time because the bus ran late."
"My life is ruined because I was brought up in a dysfunctional family."
"Nobody likes me."

Everybody has disappointments, hurts, and betrayals, but we can't let them hold us back. What we think, say, and do is creating our experience. If we think we are a victim, say we are a victim, and act as if we are a victim, we will experience being a victim in spite of the fact that we are not.

If, for example, your girlfriend or wife leaves you for another man, don't waste any time condemning the man because "he knew we were together." I know it is emotionally hard, but we don't own our partner and we can't control his or her decisions. We can only control how we handle ourselves.

Blaming and talking negatively about someone else not only won't fix your relationship issues, it won't make you feel good either because you will feel a victim and out of control with the situation. It is good to grieve and express frustration, and by all means talk to your friends and a counselor if you feel it would be beneficial for you. But after you have done all that, there is no point seeking revenge or continuing to look back at what happened because you can't change it, and you will be holding yourself in a vibration that won't allow good things to come your way. Physically, resentment hurts our bodies too.

◆ ◆ ◆

There are certain tasks that bring greater responsibility for taking care of many people, such as raising children, or being the head of a police department. We are also responsible for the earth, the environment, and how we take care of all animals and plants.

Make sure to take responsibility when it is yours to take.

When and what should you not take responsibility for?

When we are in a habit of rescuing people, we take away their power. If for example, you have a grown up child who is constantly demanding money, by continually fulfilling his wishes you will be taking away his power to resolve the challenges in his life.

Sometimes we think we are responsible for someone else's situation or state of mind, but this is not true. Everybody is responsible for their own happiness or misfortune, and this is a blessing because it provides everyone with the power to create and change their own reality if they wish to do so.

The Law of Responsibility teaches us that we need to know when we cross the line between being responsible for ourselves, and taking somebody else's responsibility. When we don't want to tell somebody the truth, for example, because we think they will feel hurt, jealous, or depressed, we are projecting our own fears onto them and we are not giving them the option to handle the message in whatever way it is appropriate for them. We disempower people by taking on their stuff.

As I have mentioned previously, use discernment. If you have a friend who is going through a rough time, for example, if he is about to get divorced, and is asking for your help to stay with you for a while, you will probably want to help him. However, when the same friend takes the offer and stays for many months, and relies on you for food and comfort, then you might be taking on too many of his issues. Your intuition will guide you to know when you feel you are taking on more of other people's problems than you should.

We also need to be careful not to create negative karma for ourselves. If we assist another soul with love without expecting anything in return, we will reap rewards. However, if we are repeatedly taking too much responsibility for somebody else out of our own need to feel wanted and loved, then we create negative karma.

It is also incorrect to force our help and advice on other people. It is true that sometimes people don't know how to ask for help, and again you should use your discernment to figure out if you should step in to provide assistance. However, usually, if people are not asking for help, then they don't need it, or they might not need it from you. Do not assume you know what they need or how they feel. You might have struggled in their situation, but that doesn't mean they feel the pain in the same way, or they want a way out now. Their path might mean the assistance comes later, or from another person.

When we allow people to take responsibility for their lives, we empower them; when we learn to discern when to take action or not, we grow spiritually.

Let go of drama

Do not give permanent reality to temporary things

EMMANUEL'S BOOK I

Sometimes we focus and fuss over things we can't control and that are not important. Our trip can be ruined by the weather, the delayed plane, or the rude waiter. All of these things are of course annoyances, but we don't have to let them "ruin everything." Sometimes we get upset over the smallest things.

There is power in putting our problems into perspective. We can reframe our world with a positive or different perspective. Would you feel the same about the delayed flight, the weather on that trip, or the bad traffic on your way to work if your spouse had just told you she was leaving you? Or that she had a serious illness?

I recommend a great book called *Don't Sweat the Small Stuff... and It's All Small Stuff*, by Richard Carlson. It contains 100 simple ways to keep the little things from taking over our lives. *Don't Sweat the Small Stuff* contains excellent reminders to care about what is important, and it gives great advice about not letting things get to us.

Most situations are not as bad as they seem, but we make them harder by repeatedly thinking about them and "making a mountain out of a molehill." Ask yourself often: Does this really matter? Is this still going to be important in a month's time?

14

How Not to Sabotage
Your Own Manifesting

Whether you think you can, or think you can't, you are right

HENRY FORD

D O YOU FEEL you have done it all, followed every step, and
you are still not getting what you want? There are various
ways in which you may be subconsciously sabotaging your
own desires.

Condemning money, or people with money

One possible reason people don't have more money is because they
are silently or openly condemning it. They want money, yet they refer
to it as "filthy lucre" or "the root of all evil." You should never
criticize money because you are sending mixed messages to your
subconscious mind: "I want to be rich, but people with expensive
things are greedy or corrupt, or not spiritual."

Don't waste your time getting annoyed and frustrated with the "world" when your time could be spent on much more productive things. It is unproductive to spend time on Facebook sharing photos, news, and posts about how unfair the world is, or how much it costs the tax payer if the royal family goes on vacation. The royal family, rich families, and everybody else on this Earth are fulfilling the role they came to do, and they have nothing to do with you or your manifestation abilities.

I'm not saying that you shouldn't stand up for what you believe is right, or raise awareness about a specific topic that is dear to your heart. What I'm saying is that criticizing for the sake of it, and fighting wealth, will not get you closer to your goals. Feeling jealous or resentful of the success of others, even the wealth attained by birthright, is only going to keep you where you are. If you feel, "this is unfair" or "my life is unfair" or "the world is unfair," you will not be able to experience anything else but unfairness.

Use your energy to move closer toward meeting your goals, and remove all other distractions. What people should, or should not do with their money, is none of your business. Take charge of the things you can control, and let go of the rest.

Worrying and fearing the worse, negative self talk

My life has been filled with terrible misfortunes,
most of which never happened

MICHEL DE MONTAIGNE

How many times have you worried about something that never came about? Do you obsess over what-ifs?

The irrational worrying feeling is sometimes so intense that our intention to eradicate it is not enough; still, you have probably realized from personal experience that most of your worries have never happened, and they probably never will.

Remember the power of repetition and how it affects our mind. Do you command yourself repeatedly to worry? How often do you say to yourself, or others, "I am a natural worrier. I worry all the time." Or do you say to others: "This job will never make me rich, but it pays the bills," or "I just want to live comfortably, I don't ask for much," then you will get just enough to pay the bills, and not much more.

The best way to change your thinking is to choose a better feeling thought and start affirming the opposite of your concerns. Every time you start worrying you could begin to choose a different command, such as "I can see peace instead of this."

In *Feel the Fear and Do It Anyway*, Susan Jeffers explains there are three types of fears:

1. Level 1 fears are those that "happen": aging, being alone, making decisions, changing career, etc.
2. Level 2 fears are those that involve the ego: failure, rejection, success, etc.
3. Level 3 fears say: "I can't handle it!"

She explains that at the bottom of every one of our fears there is simply the fear that we won't be able to handle whatever life may bring us. She says that the truth is that we can and will handle it, but we just think we can't.

I read this book in my twenties and it was a great help for me. There are other books on the market that can help you with fears, and some approaches might work better than others. I have read only a few, but *Feel the Fear and Do It Anyway* is the one that had the biggest and most positive impact on me.

In some cases, specific therapy like seeing a hypnotherapist might work better than a book. (An irrational fear of water is very different from the fear of not being good enough.) It depends on what you need to work on within the fear spectrum in order to achieve your goals.

Not addressing your problems and weaknesses

Not addressing your problems and weaknesses can be a big road block on your path. Look for patterns that repeat themselves:

1. You are always late for meetings and dates.

2. You never get things done, you procrastinate, or you have countless incomplete projects. If you carry a belief such as, "I never get things finished," determine what is worth pursuing and what is worth letting go.

Apparently, we only complete 41% of the items on our to-do lists. All those undone items lead to stress and insomnia because of the Zeigarnik effect, which in essence means uncompleted tasks will stay in our mind until we finish them. (People remember incomplete or interrupted tasks better than completed tasks.) Make a list of everything you can think of that is incomplete; decide what stays on the list and what you can delegate or completely let go. Make it a priority to finish the tasks that remain in the list.

3. You wait for "the perfect time" every time you try to start something big. Waiting for the perfect time to do anything is usually counterproductive (for example, waiting for your kids to go to college, for your partner to change, or to live in the right house, or city). Circumstances are never going to be 100% to your liking before you make a move. In fact, quite the opposite: You have to take action in order for the circumstances to move in the direction of your dreams. Stop waiting for the perfect moment. I love the following quote by Sheldon Kopp, American Psychotherapist, and author:

I have never begun any important venture
for which I felt adequately prepared.

I feel that way every time I approach something new.

4. You repeatedly change your mind.

5. You repeatedly avoid responsibility by justifying your problems with excuses like "Everybody has debt" or by justifying your limitations with "I'm not pretty enough, thin enough, tall enough, young enough, or clever enough to attempt this or that."

6. You live in denial: "All teenagers behave like that."

7. You have poverty consciousness. Many studies show how most people who get sudden large sums of money, either via inheritance or from winning the lottery, lose it all or spend it all in a short amount of time. The reason for this behavior is because they feel poor inside and therefore subconsciously they are reflecting outwardly what is going on internally. Abundance is an attitude; it is not the attainment of stuff that causes us to be abundant, it is our mindset. You might pile up your garage with Ferraris and still feel poor.
There is a big difference between being poor and not having enough money at a given moment in time. Poor is a state of mind rooted in a belief in lack. Not having money at a particular moment is a temporary situation.

I'm far from perfect. I have bad days. I change my mind. I procrastinate. I wish I would think more before talking, and I certainly don't think positively all the time. (As a matter of fact, the statement "think positively and all your problems will be gone," is neither helpful nor true.) The key point is, if you don't address your problems and weaknesses, and if it happens too often and bothers you, then deal with them because they are keeping you away from fulfilling your goals, and therefore are stopping abundance from flowing to you.

15

Tools for Everyday Living

*Real difficulties can be overcome; it is only
the imaginary ones that are unconquerable.*

THEODORE NEWTON VAIL

The power of a tidy house

YOU MIGHT BE wondering what your house has to do with anything. How can the cleanliness and tidiness of your house be relevant to finding happiness, manifesting a partner, getting your dream job, or attaining peace of mind? Well, it has a lot to do with it.

In a study[10] called *Interactions of Top-Down and Bottom-Up Mechanisms in Human Visual Cortex,* researchers found that when our environment is cluttered, the visual chaos restricts our ability to focus, and our brain

---

[10] "Interactions of Top-Down and Bottom-Up Mechanisms in Human Visual Cortex," The Journal of

Neuroscience (12 January 2011, 31 (2) 587-597). http://www.jneurosci.org/content/31/2/587.long

is unable to process information easily because the clutter is too distracting. When we clear our clutter, we clear our mind.

Having a serene, peaceful home alleviates feelings of agitation and restlessness that the clutter precipitates in our brain. Maintaining an uncluttered, peaceful home can make us feel more energetic and relaxed at the same time. Most people feel better in an uncluttered environment.

The things that are more in harmony with who we are now will more easily flow into our lives. Our physical body also reacts to our environment. Although it is very good to follow every step we can to do our inner work and feel better in the process, it is equally important to choose a living environment that supports our new vibration.

We should aim to clean and tidy our home and all our possessions, since every item we own carries a vibration: our closets, our garage, cars, purses, wallets, etc. When we let one thing go, it leaves an energy void. The universe abhors an empty space and immediately fills it, which leads us toward where we want to be or what we want to have. If we are asking for new clothes, we need to clear out our old, unworn clothes. That will physically and energetically open the space for the new to arrive.

The importance of a tidy house has been understood for centuries by followers of Feng Shui, an ancient Chinese art of creating a harmonious environment by balancing the energies in our living space. Feng Shui is based on the premise that our environment, how we place objects, and what type they are, impact our wealth, health, and joy. Arguments, swearing, and very negative thoughts and people lower the vibration of those things around them, whereas beautiful, inspiring thoughts, and conversations raise their frequency.

My favorite book on this subject is the bestseller, *The Life Changing Magic of Tidying Up: The Japanese Art of Decluttering and Organizing*, by Marie Kondo. She explains that the key to happiness is to keep the things that bring us joy personally and to discard the rest. The idea is that we concentrate on what we want to keep. She has six rules for tidying up, which I thought they were very clever and that worked well for me.

The first time I did a really good clear-out I felt like a big burden had been lifted from my shoulders. I was so relieved to finally part with things I had been keeping needlessly for decades "just in case." It was cluttering my living space and my mind, yet I had not been noticing that.

On a side note, it is possible that you can become healthy, happy, and successful while living in a pit of clutter, particularly if you believe that you can be totally successful no matter what. Belief in and of itself is one of the most important keys to succeed. However, this is more the exception than the rule. Clean up your space and see your life change!

Fake it till you make it!

The faster way to become who you want to be is to pretend you already are it. If, for example, you want to be more patient or humble, start behaving like a really humble and patient person. "What would Jesus do?"

In 2016 I saw a brilliant TED[11] talk by Amy Cuddy, author of *Presence: Bringing Your Boldest Self to Your Biggest Challenges.* TED is a non-profit organization devoted to spreading ideas, usually in the form of short, powerful talks.

Cuddy says that merely assuming a "power pose" – for example, standing like Wonder Woman – can change your body chemistry and make you feel more confident in anxiety induced situations such as interviews, first dates, or giving a talk.

You can use this technique in multiple scenarios. Don't wait until one day when you magically feel more confident. Try this instead and see your confidence grow.

---

[11] TED http://www.ted.com/talks/amy_cuddy_your_body_language_shapes_who_you_are#t-94180

Behave as successful people do

Success is a way of being; it is not something that happens by chance. Success is being happy and content with who we are and what we do, and it is something we attract because of the person we have become. It can only be measured relative to our desires (fulfillment of relationships, peace of mind, health, financial abundance).

In the book, *The One thing: The Surprisingly Simple Truth Behind Extraordinary Results*, Gary Keller writes that we can become successful with less discipline than we think we need, for one simple reason: Success is about doing the right thing, not about doing everything right.

Success has its own frequency. In order to create what we want, we need to learn the traits of having a successful state of mind.

Common traits of successful people

- They know what they want and work at what they are passionate about. They follow their life purpose.

- They have big visions. They set goals and commit to them. They think about what they want and how to get it most of the time.

- They learn to work harder on themselves than on their jobs. They are not better than we are, but they have probably put more practice, more study, and more thought into achieving what they want than we have. They become the best in their fields by reading, learning, attending workshops, associating themselves with winners, and growing. They make their best effort.

- They are action-oriented people who don't sit and wait for their life to happen.

- They follow their intuition, or gut instinct.

  Steve Jobs, American entrepreneur and co-founder of Apple, Inc., said: "Your time is limited, so don't waste it living someone else's life. Don't be trapped by dogma – which is living with the results of other people's thinking. Don't let the noise of others' opinions drown out your own inner voice. And, most important, have the courage to follow your heart and intuition. They somehow already know what you truly want to become. Everything else is secondary."

- They take responsibility for what happens to them and their businesses.

- They don't feel they need to be right at all costs. They are more committed to finding out why things are going wrong, and fixing them, than they are of defending their own position and maintaining their ignorance.

- They are optimistic. They have a positive mental attitude toward themselves and others.

- They know, or have learned, how to be assertive. Successful people know when to say no to anything that diverts them from their goals, and they say no frequently. Research conducted at the University of California in San Francisco shows that the more difficulty we have in saying no, the more likely we will experience stress, burnout, and even depression.

Read, Learn, Grow

Many books have this statement, attributed to different people: "Your income will grow to the extent that you do." Successful people know that.

Some people fail at their business because they haven't researched or learned everything they needed to, not just in their field but in running and growing their business. Say, for example, you are a brilliant speaker and you are at the top of your field in knowledge. However, your speaking business never seems to take off, and you don't have enough bookings for your speaking engagements. The reason is probably because you need to learn more about enrollment, how to attract clients, and how to let people know that you are wanting to share your knowledge. Look for books on that subject, attend workshops, or, if you can afford it, hire somebody who has mastered enrollment.

Ask yourself, which skill do I need to develop to be even more successful at my job?

Inner work is very important too. The better you feel inside, the better your life will become. If you try to manifest through action alone, you are ignoring the inner transformation that is a prerequisite for change. Investing in your personal growth and spiritual path is probably one of the best decisions you can make.

Your talents, intelligence, and memory can also be developed through effort and practice. An excellent book to improve your memory is *Unlimited Memory: How to Use Advanced Learning Strategies to Learn Faster, Remember More and Be More Productive,* by Grandmaster Kevin Horsley. Horsley is one of only a few people in the world to have received the title *International Grandmaster of Memory.*

I have read hundreds of wonderful books, and I'm mentioning many of them in this book. The following books are some of my all time favorites in self help, personal growth, and spiritual categories. I have listed them in case you want to start reading these subjects but are lost in the choices. Use your intuition to select which ones you might enjoy.

In no particular order:

1. *Living with Joy: Keys to Personal Power and Spiritual Transformation,* and *Creating Money: Attracting Abundance,* by Sanaya Roman
2. *Angels in My Hair: The True Story of a Modern-Day Irish Mystic,* by Lorna Byrne
3. *Journey of Souls: Case Studies of Life Between Lives,* and *Destiny of Souls: New Case Studies of Life Between Lives,* by Michael Newton
4. *One Last Time: A Psychic Medium Speaks to Those We Have Loved and Lost,* by John Edward
5. *The Awakener: The Time Is Now,* by Sandy Stevenson
6. *Ask and It Is Given: Learning to Manifest Your Desires,* by Esther and Jerry Hicks
7. *A Little Light on the Spiritual Laws* and *New Light on Angels: Updated Edition of "A Little Light on Angels,"* by Diana Cooper
8. *The Source Field Investigations: The Hidden Science and Lost Civilizations Behind the 2012 Prophecies,* by David Wilcock
9. *Conversations with God: An Uncommon Dialogue, Book 1* and *Home with God,* by Neale Donald Walsch
10. *Emmanuel's Book: A Manual for Living Comfortably in the Cosmos,* by Pat Rodegast and Judith Stanton
11. *Feel the Fear and Do It Anyway: Dynamic Techniques for Turning Fear, Indecision and Anger into Power, Action and Love,* by Susan Jeffers
12. *The Success Principles: How to Get from Where You Are to Where You Want to Be,* by Jack Canfield and Janet Switzer
13. *The Life Changing Magic of Tidying Up: The Japanese Art of Decluttering and Organizing,* by Marie Kondo

Live as if you were to die tomorrow. Learn as if you were to live forever.

MAHATMA GANDHI

Part III
Healing Body and Soul

16

The Human Energy Field

Knowing yourself is the beginning of all wisdom

ARISTOTLE

IN THE SAME manner that we are all contained within the Field of Consciousness, a human being is also contained within an energy field, commonly called a light body, or aura. Our light body is our energetic duplicate.

This energy field, combined with our consciousness, determines the health and balance of our mind, body, and spirit. It surrounds a normal, healthy person in an egg shape and extends five to eight feet around the body.

As well as the aura, our body also has two subtle energy systems through which energy flows: meridians (body energy pathways) and chakras (body energy centers). All three emit electromagnetic energy and light.

Meridians

In traditional Chinese medicine, meridians are invisible energy pathways or channels that run through the body. Our vital life energy, also called *qi* or *chi*, is thought to flow along these meridians; and when this circulation becomes stagnant, blocked, or out of balance, illness results. These meridians flow through all of the major organs. Traditional Chinese medicine uses acupuncture as a technique for balancing this life force (qi) by placing extremely thin needles at specific points along these meridians. By harmonizing and balancing the flow of this energy, the acupuncturist believes that the energy flow will re-balance.

Chakras

The human body has energy stations located throughout the body, referred to as *chakras. Chakra* is a Sanskrit word that means "wheel." Each chakra is associated with a certain part of the body and a certain organ that provides the energy it needs to function. To be healthy, our seven main chakras need to stay open, aligned, and fluid. If there is a blockage, energy cannot flow.

Some books refer to the existence of seven main chakras which are located along the spine and extend out the front and back of the body. Current books talk about seven main chakras that run throughout the body, plus five more chakras: Three higher trans-personal chakras at the back of the head, one Soul Star chakra about six inches above the head, and one more Stellar Gateway chakra about twelve inches above the head, for a total of twelve.

The chakra system originated in India between 1500 and 500 BC in an ancient Hindu text called *Vedas*. Through the chakra system, the aura layers transmit information between the body and the immediate external environment. Each chakra corresponds to a layer of the aura and has a number of specific qualities. The lower chakras are associated with fundamental emotions and needs and vibrate at a lower frequency, while the upper chakras vibrate quicker and correspond to our higher mental and spiritual aspirations and faculties.

The human energy field – the work of Dr. Burr

Harold Saxton Burr, Ph.D., Professor of Anatomy at Yale University School of Medicine, discovered that all living things, plants, trees, animals, and human beings possess energy fields, or what he termed *Fields of Life,* or *L-Fields.* He was able to demonstrate an accurate and repeatable technique for measuring these fields using standard voltmeters.

In his book, *Blueprint for Immortality: The Electric Patterns of Life,* Burr claimed that the life field of all living things molds and controls each organism's development, health, and mood. Dr. Burr published, either alone or with others, more than 93 scientific papers and made thousands of measurements. He postulated that these fields are the blueprints of all life on Earth.

Some of his findings were:

- Every living thing possesses an L- Field.

- All diseases show up in a body's energy field, not only while disease is present but even before symptoms arise. In *Hands of Light: A Guide to Healing Through the Human Energy Field,* Barbara Ann Brennan explains how energy events within the auric field are primary to and always precede (precipitate) a physical event. That means that any illness will show first in the human field (aura) before it shows in the physical body.

- People's emotional stability can be determined by looking at their L-Field. Based on over 30,000 measurements on human beings, the higher the reading, the better the subject was feeling, and vice versa.

- Cancer and other diseases can accurately be predicted well in advance by measuring voltage gradients. Burr's voltmeter technology was extended to cancer populations in two publications that were reported in the mainstream journals *American Journal of Obstetrics* and *Gynecology and Science.*[12]

The L-Field (aura) has also been captured in Kirlian photography. Semyon Davidovich Kirlian was a Russian inventor and researcher who discovered that passing a high frequency electrical current through an object while photographing it revealed an image surrounded by a bright luminous aura. The resulting image of the object with its colored aura around it was able to indicate stress, illness, and other mental, emotional, and physiological issues according to the colors, clarity, size, and shape of the aura.

Numerous healers have associated the aura with a person's health and well-being, and this was corroborated by the work of Dr. Burr. The aura, and changes within it, reflects physical, emotional, mental, and spiritual aspects of the individual. Weakened auras can result in and reflect feelings of failure and health problems.

Kirlian's first scientific paper on Kirlian photography was published in 1961, in the *Russian Journal of Scientific and Applied Photography*. In 1949, Semyon Kirlian and his wife received a Soviet patent on their device: "A method of photographing by means of high-frequency currents." They claimed that Kirlian photography could provide clues to a person's physical health and could illuminate the acupuncture points of the human body. Light can be photographed coming out of the hands of healers too.

The characteristics of the aura, or Field of Energy

The aura has seven main layers, each of them relating to the physical, mental, emotional, and spiritual aspects of the human being. The layers are arranged one inside the other. The speed and vibration of energy is increased on each level.

---

[12] Langman & Burr, 1947, 1949

We can feel the aura when we realize that the space we occupy doesn't end with the physical body. Often we feel uncomfortable when somebody is too close to us, "in our face." Being in large crowds also poses a challenge for some people.

Each level of the aura is connected to our seven main chakras:

1. *First Layer: The Etheric Body.* This is the energy closest to the physical body and the densest. It transmits energies from the higher bodies down to our physical body. It is stronger when we have our basic needs covered, like food and shelter. It is connected to the first chakra, the root chakra.

2. *Second Layer: The Emotional Body.* This layer affects our emotional balance. All our emotions, such as happiness, contentment, grief, sadness, and hate are found here. The second layer becomes weaker at times of emotional distress. It also includes a full range of desires, from completely selfish and destructive ones to high spiritual aspirations and the desire to help others. It is connected to the second chakra, the navel chakra.

3. *Third Layer: The Mental Body.* This layer is connected to our conscious state of mind, thoughts, memories, and reasoning skills. Its vibration is finer and higher than that of the emotional layer. Mental health or mental illness is reflected in this level. It is connected to the third chakra, the solar plexus chakra.

4. *Fourth Layer: The Astral Level.* This layer is the bridge between the denser, lower vibrations of the subtle layers, and the higher layers of spiritual vibrations. It shows our capacity for unconditional love; it becomes stronger through loving relationships and weaker during conflicts or break ups.
The astral level connects us to the higher dimensions of reality: near death experiences, hallucinations, experiences outside the

body, and imagination. It is activated by meditation, and it is connected to the fourth chakra, the heart chakra.

The next three layers are contained in what are referred to as the spiritual aspects of the human being:

5. *Fifth Layer: The Etheric Template Body.* In this layer we store the present and all the possible futures. It can be made stronger by expressing our truth and knowing who we are. It is connected to the fifth chakra, the throat chakra.

6. *Sixth Layer: The Celestial Body.* This layer gives access to higher feelings (bliss, spiritual ecstasy), thoughts, and manifestations. When this body is developed through raising awareness, personal growth, and creative visualization, it can be extremely powerful in connecting us with our purpose in life. It is connected to the sixth chakra, the third eye chakra.

7. *Seventh Layer: The Ketheric Template or Causal Body.* This is the farthest away from the physical body. It contains the soul's plan for our life and reflects all the knowledge and experiences that the soul has gained during the current and prior lifetimes. It is associated with divine and universal consciousness. The energies in this body spin with a very high frequency, and it is the strongest and most resistant layer. This layer contains all the other layers within it. It is connected to the seventh chakra, the crown chakra.

If you wish to learn more about the human aura, chakras, and items covered in this chapter, I recommend:

- *Hands of Light: A Guide to Healing Through the Human Energy Field*, by Barbara Ann Brennan
- *Energy Medicine: Balancing Your Body's Energies for Optimal Health, Joy and Vitality*, by Donna Eden and David Feinstein

17

Causes of Disease

If you jog every morning, eat nothing but health food, avoid sugar, haven't smoked in years, make sure you get enough sleep, and drink only bottled water, yet you do that from a place of anxiety, you are not in any way maintaining your health. You are merely not heeding what it is that will, at some time, make you ill – which is fear.

EMMANUEL'S BOOK II

DEPENDING ON THE culture we come from, or the philosophy we believe in, there are many reasons we get sick and also a myriad of ways to treat our afflictions.

We saw in the previous chapter that in addition to our physical body we also have three subtle energy systems:

1. The aura, light body, or energy field. The aura contains seven layers that relate to the four aspects of the human being: physical, emotional, mental, and spiritual.
2. Meridians (body energy pathways).
3. Chakras (body energy centers).

The best way to understand what is causing a disease is to find a healing system, or a theory, that considers the human being as a mind-body-spirit system, not merely a compound of muscles, bones, organs, tissues, and nerves.

Over the centuries and throughout the world we can find numerous references to whole body systems of healing, like traditional Chinese medicine and Indian Ayurveda. These systems understand that mind and body are connected, and that the body has an energy field that needs to be taken care of in order to be at optimal health (or to regain it). Experience and ancient knowledge have taught them that the cause of disease is not always merely physical; there are other mental and spiritual factors to be considered.

A comprehensive explanation of the causes of disease can also be found in the work of Paracelsus, a 1493 Swiss alchemist, physician, astrologer, and philosopher, and the founder of modern toxicology.

He believed that a human being has two bodies: a visible body that belongs to the earth, and an invisible body of heaven. He postulated the existence of five reasons disease could be present in the body. He also connected disease to emotion; however, he believed that not every disease had to have a corresponding emotional problem.

Let's explore traditional Chinese Medicine, Ayurveda, and Paracelsus further.

Traditional Chinese Medicine (TCM)

Traditional Chinese medicine (TCM) is a healing system of Eastern medicine developed in China more than 2,000 years ago. TCM draws on the belief that qi ("vital energy" or "chi") is essential for overall health. TCM practitioners see disease as the result of disruptions in the circulation of qi.

The primary goal of TCM is to create wholeness and harmony within a person, allowing the mind/body/spirit to heal itself. They assess three major items in a person:

1. The patient's external factors or environment (seasons, weather).
2. The patient's emotional state, and how they can help them manage stress in a healthy way.
3. The patient's lifestyle (exercise, diet).

In TCM, emotions and physical health are intimately connected. They view our emotions as impacting our vital organs. Anger affects the liver. Worry and over-thinking affects the spleen and digestion. Sadness and grief harm the lungs. Fear damages the kidney. Shock disorients the qi of the heart, spleen, and kidney. Every emotion that is not properly digested and dealt with is stored within the heart, muscles, and fibers within our body, which in turn causes various ailments to appear in our lives.

To restore the qi, TCM practitioners are trained to use a variety of ancient and modern therapeutic methods, including acupuncture, herbal medicine, massage, nutrition, and lifestyle counseling.

Ayurveda

Ayurvedic medicine is a system of healing that originated in ancient India. In Sanskrit, *ayur* means "life" or "living," and *veda* means "knowledge," so Ayurveda has been defined as the "knowledge of living" or the "science of longevity."

According to Ayurvedic theory, everything in the universe is connected; therefore, anything that affects our physical, spiritual, or emotional well-being can cause us to be out of balance with the universe. Good health is achieved when our mind, body, and spirit are in harmony with the universe.

Deepak Chopra, MD, a world-renowned pioneer in integrative medicine and personal transformation, says that the two main guiding principles of Ayurveda are that (a) the mind and the body are connected, and (b) nothing has more power to heal and transform the body than the mind.

Chopra explains[13] that meditation is just one of the most powerful tools the ancient Ayurvedic physicians prescribed for balancing the mind and body. Ayurveda also offers many other practices for expanding self-awareness and cultivating your innate state of balance, such as nutrition, counseling, massage, natural medications, and herbal remedies.

Paracelsus

Paracelsus, born Philippus Aureolus Theophrastus Bombastus Von Hohenheim, believed that the human being is a representation, on a smaller scale, of all that is contained in the world.

He claimed there are five major causes of illness: The first three causes deal with the body, and the last two belong to the spirit. He said that if the body suffers, the spirit need not suffer, but if the spirit suffers, then the body will suffer. The body cannot live without the spirit, but the spirit is not confined to the body and therefore is independent of it.

Illness can be a complex interaction of all five causes. An isolated winter cold or flu may not mean much at all, but continued colds all year long, year after year, may have a root in emotional or spiritual issues. Although it will be right to treat the current cold, it will be more desirable to find a long term solution by considering all five causes of disease:

1. External and environmental: epidemics, floods, earthquakes, heat, cold, and rain.
2. Poisonous substances and impurities: toxic fumes, spoiled food, chemicals of all kinds, and medicines with side effects.
3. Living habits and lifestyle: malnutrition, unhealthy diet, alcohol, and drugs.
4. Psychological causes: mental and emotional issues.

---

[13] http://www.chopra.com/articles/what-is-ayurveda#sm.000000kwsu0fvlcslw3i4ogqu53oy

5. Spiritual (karma): Disease is the effect of a previously existing cause created in this life or during a former existence.

1. External and environmental

You were probably told when you were young not to play outside in the rain or you would get sick. That's an example of external influences invading the body and causing illness.

In traditional Chinese medicine, if the wind enters the body, qi will flow erratically. It will stagnate qi in one place and then quickly move to another. If a person is already weak, seasonal changes may invade and cause illness.

2. Poisonous substances and impurities

These are: poisonous substances and impurities taken in food and drink, inhaled in the air, or absorbed in the skin: toxic fumes, spoiled food, chemicals of all kinds, medicines with side effects, etc.

The term *side effect* is somehow misleading; it seems to be considered synonymous with unimportant. For some drugs the side effect can be very serious, like giving you a stroke; there is nothing "side" about that. Also, some short-term, apparently insignificant side effects can have adverse long-term consequences.

Dr. Bruce H. Lipton, Ph.D., a renowned cell biologist, in his book *The Biology of Belief: Unleashing the Power of Consciousness, Matter and Miracles,* writes that when a drug is introduced into the body to treat a malfunction in one protein, that drug inevitably interacts with at least one and possibly many other proteins. He can see why pharmaceutical drugs come with information sheets listing voluminous side effects that range from irritating to deadly. In Dr. Lipton's words:

Because we are not powerless biochemical machines, popping a pill every time we are mentally or physically out of tune is not the answer. Drugs and surgery are powerful tools when they are not overused, but the notion of simple drug fixes is fundamentally flawed. Every time a drug is introduced into the body to correct function A, it inevitably throws off function B, C, or D. It is not gene-directed hormones and neurotransmitters that control our bodies and our minds; our beliefs control our bodies, our minds and thus our lives.

Lipton demonstrates how the new science of epigenetics is revolutionizing our understanding of the link between mind and matter, and the profound effects it has on our personal lives and the collective life of our species. I really enjoyed reading *The Biology of Belief*.

3. Living habits and lifestyle

These are destructive living habits and lifestyle: malnutrition, unhealthy diet, alcohol, and drugs.

Body conditions like hunger, or too much food or alcohol, affect our mental and emotional states with great intensity. For example, too much sugar and nutritionally lacking food can cause depression, lack of sleep, or hunger, which can make it difficult for us to concentrate. Sometimes changing our diet and eating wholesome food dramatically improves our mood and decreases the size of our problems. The impact of adequate nutrition on our physical well-being is addressed in Chapter 21.

4. Psychological causes, mental, and emotional

Stress results from our emotional response to situations and conditions: grief, fear, sadness, overthinking, shock, psychological trauma, disordered thoughts, morbid imagination, hysteria, and other emotional conditions.

A lot has been written about the effects of our mental state on our physical body, and several great books explain how our unresolved emotional issues appear in the body as disease. One of the best books in this field is the classic *You Can Heal Your Life*, by Louise Hay.

In this field of thought, disease occurs when the body's energy is not flowing smoothly. Fear, hurt, resentment, hate, grief, anger, and jealousy vibrate at a very low level, which keeps our energy stuck. For healing to occur, we need to heal our emotions so the flow of energy through the body can be restored.

Illness starts in the spiritual and emotional bodies, cascading down and settling themselves as blockages in the physical body. Basically, in this category, the reason for our illness goes deeper than just a mere physical dysfunction.

Deeply ingrained beliefs or habits – about what is right and wrong about ourselves – also contribute to the development of emotional blockages and thus the manifestation of illness: "I'm worthless," or "Nobody loves me." Since illness represents a stuck emotion, it is not always easy to understand what the disease or the symptom represents.

In the late 1970's, a new field in medicine known as psychoneuro-immunology (PNI) emerged, studying the interaction between our psychological (mental) processes and our physiology (the nervous and immune systems of the human body). This is what is commonly known as *the mind-body* connection.

In 1985, a neuro-pharmacologist named Candace Pert, research professor in the Department of Physiology and Biophysics at Georgetown University School of Medicine, and author of *Molecules of Emotion: The Science Behind Mind-Body Medicine*, revealed that neuropeptide-specific receptors are present on the cell walls of both the brain and the immune system, which means that the chemicals triggered by emotions physically interact with cells and tissues in our bodies. When we repeatedly picture our worst-case scenarios and worry to no end, we generate a chemical imbalance which in turn creates disease in the body.

More recent studies have shown unquestionable links between our thoughts, the stress response, and both our susceptibility to illness and our capacity to heal. The closer we study the body, the more we discover the direct connection between how we think and how we feel.

Please note, if you have a serious mental condition, it is as important to follow the appropriate `therapy and to take the medicine you need as outlined by your physician, psychologist, psychiatrist, or relevant doctor. Regardless of what your emotional issues are, you should never dismiss the importance of adequately treating brain chemical imbalances.

5. Spiritual (karma)

Diseases originating from karma are the most difficult to diagnose because it is not simply the period between birth and the disease to consider; the disease might relate to karma brought forward from previous lives. Energy healing, praying, or hypnotherapy to uncover prior lives might assist healing, particularly when you have tried everything else and "nothing" seems to be working.

Don't overthink

Although it is helpful to understand the reasons behind our sickness, it is important not to overthink which one of the five reasons caused it. We don't have to over analyze and find emotional and spiritual reasons for every single ailment of the body.

Kathryn Hansen, in her book *Brain Over Binge: Why I Was Bulimic, Why Conventional Therapy Didn't Work, and How I Recovered for Good*, explains how she was told by her therapists that her binge eating was only a symptom of a deeper issue, such as low self esteem, depression, anxiety, and family and social issues. But she didn't think that she had any of those problems. She says that regardless of what she uncovered from her past, what she resolved in the present, or how she envisioned her future, her urges to binge eat still consumed her. She didn't want to go to more therapy, attend support groups, or follow meal plans. Regardless of the amount of traditional therapy that she received, she continued binging.

Her book is an amazing tale of how she recovered from bulimia on her own, without having to find, or actually have, any psychological or emotional reason behind her disorder.

In order to fully heal, we need to take care of our mind, body, and spirit. We will discuss conventional medicine and alternative therapies in the next chapter.

18

Conventional Medicine
and Alternative Therapies

There are hundreds of paths up the mountain,
all leading to the same place, so it doesn't matter which path you
take. The only person wasting time is the one who runs around
the mountain, telling everyone that his or her path is wrong.

HINDU PROVERB

WHEN IT COMES to the use of conventional versus alternative therapies we have gone to extremes, and extremes are not balanced options. Some people have never tried and will never try alternative therapies, branding them all "inefficient" and "a con," while other people swear by them so much that they won't contemplate conventional medicine, citing the "big pharmaceutical agenda" and all drug treatments as dangerous for the body.

The reason I believe that so many people distrust alternative practices is because some dishonest practitioners that are associated with them; some individuals and corporations have taken financial advantage of sick and vulnerable people looking for alternative hope outside of conventional medicine. That has given the entire alternative medicine community a bad reputation. The eagerness of some alternative practitioners to bash conventional medicine has not helped either.

The word *alternative* is misleading. In the Western side of the world it seems to imply something unscientific and superstitious, but in many other cultures, particularly in the Far East, this alternative medicine is their conventional medicine.

Conventional medicine has evolved, and has better refined the use of drugs and surgical technology. It can be life saving in many situations. People survive brain tumors, life-threatening allergic reactions, and serious injuries because of the advances in medicine and the types of surgery available (and to correct a popular belief in some circles, medication does not hamper our spiritual advancement. Our soul grows when we practice compassion and kindness, deal with our life lessons, and take responsibility for our lives, regardless of the amount of surgeries we need to have or the amount of conventional medicine that we have to take).

One of the biggest issues with conventional therapy is that traditional surgeries and medicines will fix the problem to some extent, as in the case of heart bypass surgery, but it won't be healing. True healing will happen when we address either our high stress levels, the emotional reason that caused the heart issue, and/or make some needed lifestyle changes (if, for example, we are not getting adequate nutrition or we smoke too much). That is, we also need to deal with our mental and ethereal bodies as well as the physical.

Conventional medicine is wonderful in many cases, but it has some limitations:

- It manages and treats symptoms instead of treating the underlying causes of sickness.
- Mind-body connection and proper nutrition are often ignored.
- Each part of the body and organs are treated independently, as opposed to using a whole-body approach.

- When the physical body is very sick it, it struggles with the number of medicines it can tolerate and the medications' side effects. Even for smaller ailments, the treatment usually starts with a pill, like providing a course of antibiotics for common childhood diseases – a mild ear infection, cough, or strep throat – that could be healed with gentler approaches like using essential oils and/or homeopathy (we will discuss these and other types of alternative treatments in Chapter 19).

Alternative medicine, in contrast, considers the mental, emotional, and spiritual bodies as well as the physical environment, nutrition, and lifestyle to diagnose and assist healing. It is nothing more than treating the whole person rather than just the symptoms of disease. Tests don't need to prove that something is wrong in order for something to not function properly; if the person doesn't feel well, then he is not well.

The big limitation of alternative therapies comes with trauma and severe illnesses that undermine the mind/body's capacity to heal. Also, for emergencies, such as a broken bone, a burst appendix, or most accidents, conventional medicine is the fastest and probably the best and most efficient route to healing.

I consider alternative therapies a great complement to conventional medicine, not necessarily good as sole therapy. It depends on what we are trying to cure or achieve.

How to choose an alternative, or complementary treatment

No one method works for everybody, even if the initial diagnoses seem similar. Each healing modality has a specific frequency, and each person is unique and carries a specific frequency too. Understanding how we contracted the disease ultimately affects the treatment required.

There are various reasons some healing modalities work for some people and not for others:

1. Natural preferences. You are going to be naturally drawn to particular healing modalities and not at all to others. For example, you might feel very comfortable seeing an acupuncturist, but not an energy healer. If you are afraid of a particular form of treatment, such as chemotherapy or a past-life regression technique, the resulting tension will interfere with your ability to heal. But if you are impressed with the statistical results of such a treatment, you know friends and family members who have seen positive results with it, and you are open to it, then you will significantly improve the chances of it working for you. Healing will occur to the degree that the familiarity with the treatment makes your body feel secure and helps it to relax.

2. Using the wrong therapy. Some therapies reach up to heal only a specific level of the aura. For example, chiropractic therapy reaches up through the physical body and first levels of the aura, as do herbs, drugs, and surgery. Energy healing, Reiki, meditating, sound, and crystals all reach the upper levels of the auric field and have a better chance of healing emotional/spiritual problems.

3. The life lesson you came to master, which sometimes manifests as hereditary conditions. This is the reason why some illnesses that "run in the family" are present in some members but not in others.

4. Sometimes no single therapy works because people need to get to the bottom of certain issues before they are ready to release them. They are determined to hit bottom, and there is nothing anybody can say or do that will stop their determination to go there. Hitting bottom is something they wish to do, consciously or unconsciously, because they know they will eventually re-emerge stronger than ever.

There are many types of alternative practitioners. Always check their credentials and patient reviews. There is excellent alternative education available for every viable modality. Most importantly, pay attention to how you feel about the treatment itself.

To conclude, I believe there is a time and a place for both conventional and alternative medicine, and we should seek to combine both for optimal results.

19

Types of Complementary
and Alternative Therapies

The doctor of the future will give no medicine but
will interest his patients in the care of the human frame,
in diet, and in the cause and prevention of disease.

THOMAS EDISON

THERE ARE MORE than 100 systems of alternative medicines in practice all over the world. The First World Congress of Alternative Medicines was held in Italy in 1973, convened by the Medical Faculty of the University of Rome.

Within the USA, there are 50 institutions that uses some form of alternative therapy, although they use the word *integrative* in their name; for example, Harvard, Stanford, Duke, and the Mayo Clinic. Most of them offer treatments like acupuncture, massage, and nutrition counseling, along with conventional drugs and surgery.

From the American Holistic Medical Association[14] (AHMA):

The field of integrative health and medicine reaffirms the importance of the relationship between practitioner and patient, focuses on the whole person, is informed by evidence, and makes use of all appropriate therapeutic approaches, healthcare professionals, and professions to achieve optimal health and healing. Simply put, integrative health and medicine offer best practices for optimal health and healing.

There are many types of complementary and alternative therapies but it is beyond the scope of this book to explain every single one. I have listed the most popular ones in the following four groups:

1. Traditional alternative medicine: Traditional Chinese medicine, Ayurveda, naturopathy, and homeopathy.
2. Manipulative (physical) therapies: osteopathy and chiropractic.
3. Mind therapies: meditation and hypnotherapy.
4. Energy medicine: spiritual healers and Reiki, and other type of alternative therapies such as essential oils (including aroma-therapy), and reflexology.

Traditional alternative medicine

These therapies have been practiced for centuries worldwide and are the more mainstream forms of accepted therapies. These include traditional Chinese medicine, Ayurveda (we discussed both in Chapter 17), naturopathy, and homeopathy.

---

[14] http://www.holisticmedicine.org

Naturopathy

Naturopathic doctors (NDs) are physicians trained in the art and science of natural health care at accredited medical colleges. ND's prescribe natural treatments such as herbal medicine, acupuncture and other oriental remedies, hydrotherapy, and nutrition and diet.

The American Association of Naturopathic Physicians (AANP) states on its website[15]:

> Naturopathic doctors treat all medical conditions and can provide both individual and family health care. Among the most common ailments they treat are allergies, chronic pain, digestive issues, hormonal imbalances, obesity, respiratory conditions, heart disease, fertility problems, menopause, adrenal fatigue, cancer, fibromyalgia, and chronic fatigue syndrome. NDs can perform minor surgeries, such as removing cysts or stitching up superficial wounds. However, they do not practice major surgery. NDs are trained to utilize prescription drugs, although the emphasis of naturopathic medicine is the use of natural healing agents.

Hydrotherapy is the application of water for therapeutic purposes; the use of water, ice, steam, and hot and cold temperatures to maintain and restore health. Treatments include full body immersion, steam baths, saunas, and the application of hot and/or cold compresses.

Herbal therapy is an ancient form of healing still widely used in much of the world. Herbalism uses natural plants or plant-based substances to treat a range of illnesses and to enhance the functioning of the body's systems. Though herbalism is not a licensed professional modality in the United States, herbs are "prescribed" by a range of practitioners. There is a body of knowledge about the herbal treatments used by various Native Americans, and much of the

---

[15] http://www.naturopathic.org

information has been tested and incorporated into our present herbal therapies.

Some ND's are also trained in homeopathy.

Homeopathy

From the National Center for Homeopathy center[16]:

> Homeopathy is a safe, gentle, and natural system of healing that works with your body to relieve symptoms, restore itself, and improve your overall health. It is extremely safe to use, even with very small children and pets, has none of the side effects of many traditional medications, is very affordable, is made from natural substances, and is FDA regulated. It is used to treat acute illnesses, like colds, ear infections, migraines, and sore throats, as well as chronic conditions, like asthma, depression, autism, and arthritis.

Homeopathy is prescribed according to three basic principles:

1. Like cures like.
2. The more a remedy is diluted, the greater the potency.
3. Illness is specific to the individual.

Homeopathy is based on the belief that symptoms are signs of the body's effort to get rid of disease, and treatment is based on the whole person, rather than on the symptoms.

Physical therapies

Physical therapies are based on the premise that an illness or injury in one part of the body affects all parts, and that manual manipulation

---

[16] http://www.homeopathycenter.org/learn-about-homeopathy

will create and speed recovery. Touch has been used in medicine since the early days of medical care. The most commonly used types of physical therapies are osteopathy, chiropractic, and massage.

Osteopathy

Osteopathic medicine is a system of medicine based on the theory that disturbances in the musculoskeletal system affect other body parts, causing many disorders that can be corrected by various manipulative techniques in conjunction with conventional medical, surgical, pharmacological, and other therapeutic procedures. Osteopathic physicians provide comprehensive medical care, including preventive medicine, diagnosis, surgery, prescription medications, and hospital referrals.

Osteopathic Doctors (DOs) are complete physicians. That means they are fully trained and licensed to prescribe medication and to perform surgery. In diagnosis and treatment, they pay particular attention to the joints, bones, muscles, and nerves, and are specially trained in osteopathic manipulative treatment – using their hands to diagnose, treat, and prevent illness.

According to the American Osteopathic Association (AOA),[17] DOs are fully trained medical doctors (MDs) who receive additional extensive training in the body's structure and function.

Doctors of Chiropractic (DC)

The chiropractor views the spine as the backbone of human health; misalignments of the vertebrae caused by poor posture or trauma can cause pressure on the spinal nerve roots, leading to diminished function and illness. Through manipulation or adjustment of the spine, treatment seeks to analyze and correct these misalignments. Adjustments involve the manipulation of the spine and joints to re-establish and maintain normal nervous system functioning. Some

---

[17] https://www.osteopathic.org/Pages/default.aspx

chiropractors employ additional therapies, such as massage, nutrition, and applied kinesiology.

All 50 states, the District of Columbia, Puerto Rico, and the U.S. Virgin Islands officially recognize chiropractic as a health care profession. Many other countries also recognize and regulate chiropractic, including Canada, Mexico, Great Britain, Australia, Japan, and Switzerland.[18]

Mind therapies

Some healing modalities use the mind as a tool to understand the causes of disease and to treat stress and phobias. These include meditation and hypnotherapy.

Meditation

Meditation has been associated with a decrease in stress, depression, anxiety, pain, and insomnia, along with an increase in quality of life. When we meditate, we enter a state of expanded awareness and inner quiet that refreshes the mind and restores balance. When we are calm and peaceful our soul comes through our emotions to give us guidance. It also helps us to raise our vibration, which is essential to receiving our desires.

Since the mind and body are inseparable, the body is naturally balanced through the practice of meditation. Studies have shown that during meditation our heart rate and breath slow down, our body decreases the production of stress hormones, and it increases the production of neurotransmitters such as serotonin and endorphins, which enhance well-being. (Serotonin is a chemical neurotransmitter that can affect mood, appetite, sleep, and memory. Endorphins – typically released during exercise – trigger a positive feeling in the body).

---

[18] https://www.acatoday.org/About/History-of-Chiropractic

When we are under real or perceived stress, our muscles tense, our heart beat increases, vitamins and minerals are rapidly used up, and in some cases of great shock even our memory goes. All these symptoms normally subside as the body relaxes, which is also why meditation is such a great healer.

There is an ever-increasing amount of academic research[19] around the practice of meditation and its effects. Harvard neuroscientist Sara Lazar, a leading researcher in the field, was one of the first to show that when people meditate they feel better not just because they are spending time relaxing.

In 2005, Lazar and her team took Magnetic Resonance Images (MRIs) of the brain structure of sixteen study participants two weeks before and two weeks after they took part in the 8-week Mindfulness-Based Stress Reduction (MBSR) Program at the University of Massachusetts Center for Mindfulness. In addition to weekly meetings that included the practice of mindfulness meditation, participants received audio recordings for guided meditation practice and were asked to keep track of how much time they practiced each day. A set of MRI brain images was also taken of a control group of non-meditators over a similar time interval.

Lazar found that long-term meditation produced tangible changes in the brain. Participants had increases in gray matter concentration in areas of the brain associated with learning and memory processes, emotion regulation, and perspective taking.

There are numerous forms of meditation, and it is thought that prayer for the self might have an effect similar to that of meditation. The most common are:

---

[19] https://www.ncbi.nlm.nih.gov/pmc/articles/PMC3004979/;

http://news.harvard.edu/gazette/story/2011/01/eight-weeks-to-a-better-brain/

1. The traditional way: Sit quietly, focus on your breathing, and still your mind (that is, try to avoid thinking about anything).

When I started to meditate I had lots of thoughts running around and "to do" items that came and went. With practice, the noise in my head quieted down on its own. One of the best ways to detach from multiple thoughts running around in your head, and generally to reduce stress, is to practice slow, deep, rhythmic breathing. You can also keep a notebook by your side, so if you remember something important that you need to do, you can quickly write it down and keep meditating.

Some books recommend setting a timer so you don't have to check your watch, but this doesn't work for me. I stop meditating when I feel I'm either too awake, thinking too much, not connected, or bored. It can be 5 or 25 minutes, but I don't set a timer because I don't like it when the alarm goes off and I'm happily relaxed and enjoying the trance.

I usually attempt to meditate for 5-10 minutes; otherwise, the task feels too big for me. I have noticed that sometimes I will continue happily meditating for another 10 or 20 minutes, but aiming at 5 to 10 minutes makes the meditation more feasible.

Sogyal Rinpoche, in his book *The Tibetan Book of Living and Dying*, writes that what is important is not how long we meditate but ensuring that the practice brings us a state of mindfulness and presence, allowing us to enter a state in which we are a little open and able to connect with our heart presence. He says that five minutes of wakeful sitting practice is of far greater value than twenty minutes of dozing.

2. Guided meditation CDs. I highly recommend Orin and Daben meditations. You can find them on Sanaya Roman's website, *orinadaben.com,* under audio courses.[20] She has many meditations for different purposes: living your life purpose, opening to channel, creating a soul relationship, becoming a writer, etc.

---

[20] https://www.orindaben.com/catalog/echart/orin/

There are also apps and other websites that provide guided meditations, but I haven't tried them.

3. Reciting a mantra. The word mantra means "that which protects the mind" from negativity and our own mind.

Hypnotherapy

Hypnotherapy is the use of a state of focused attention, achieved through guided relaxation, to access the subconscious mind. Hypnosis is used for memory recall, medical treatment, skill enhancement, or personal growth.

Hypnotherapy is a means of bypassing the conscious mind and accessing the subconscious, where suppressed memories, repressed emotions, and forgotten events are recorded. Hypnosis may facilitate behavioral, emotional, or attitudinal change such as weight loss or smoking cessation. It is also used to treat phobias and stress.

Sometimes we have deep-rooted fears coming from previous lives, such as an irrational fear of heights, losing a loved one, or being unsuccessful. For example, death by drowning may lead to fear of being immersed in water, and a child who remembers a life that ended in shooting may show a phobia of guns and loud noises.

You will know if hypnotherapy feels right for you or not. You might want to try it if you have tried other therapies to treat phobias, stress, or other issues, without success.

Energy medicine

Energy work is beginning to be acknowledged by mainstream medicine although healing and working with energy and the Light Body is nothing new. Shamanic practitioners all over the world used Light Body healing techniques a long time ago.

Energy medicine is based on the premise that everything is energy and that changes in the life force of the body affect human health and can promote healing. Healers work by balancing the auric field.

Donna Eden's book, *Energy Medicine: Balancing Your Body's Energies for Optimal Health, Joy and Vitality* shows how to work with the electrical, electromagnetic, and subtler energies that give our body life. These energies form the foundation of our health.

If you wish to find out more information please see the American Association of Healers website[21]. You will find a wide range of energy healers in different modalities: shamanic healers, angel healers, spiritual healers, and other practices that are not purely energy healing, such as Feng Shui consultants and life coaches.

Alternatively, please visit:

* The Barbara Brennan School of healing[22]
* Donna Eden's website[23]

Reiki

Reiki is an ancient Japanese technique for stress reduction and relaxation that also promotes healing. It's administered by "laying on hands" and can easily be learned by anyone. Reiki is commonly used to treat emotional and mental distress as well as chronic and acute physical problems. It can also assist the recipient in achieving spiritual focus and clarity.

The following is an explanation of how Reiki works, from the International Center for Reiki Training:[24]

Reiki heals by flowing through the affected parts of the energy field and charging them with positive energy. It raises the vibratory level of the energy field in and around the physical body where the negative thoughts and feelings are attached. This causes

---

[21] http://americanassociationofhealers.com

[22] https://www.barbarabrennan.com

[23] http://www.innersource.net/em/about/donna-eden.html

[24] http://www.reiki.org/FAQ/HowDoesReikiWork.html

the negative energy to break apart and fall away. In so doing, Reiki clears, straightens and heals the energy pathways, thus allowing the life force to flow in a healthy and natural way.

I have received Reiki sessions and I have learned to use it for my family and myself. I have read in blogs and articles that report Reiki (and energy healing in general) to be a fraud, but from my perspective, the reasons they might view Reiki as a fraud are threefold:

1. A closed mind to any therapy outside of conventional medicine. (Ironically, many people who totally dismiss and trash Reiki have never had a session.)

2. Not every therapy works for everybody, so it could be that the people receiving Reiki didn't experience healing or the relief they were expecting.

3. The problem is the alleged practitioner and/or teacher, not Reiki. Some practitioners are better and more experienced than others, although that happens with all practitioners in both conventional and alternative medicine.

One of the best ways to find a qualified Reiki Master is to go to the International Center for Reiki Training, go to its membership listing[25], pick the state you live in, and then find a practitioner near you. Call them or go to see the practitioner you selected.

Many professional experienced Reiki practitioners are not listed with the International Center for Reiki Training (ICRT). This is because there are other ways to obtain the Reiki qualification and students don't have to go through ICRT. However, ICRT is the only Reiki organization I'm aware of that keeps a public online listing of all its practitioners.

---

[25] http://www.reikimembership.com/MembershipListing.aspx

A lot of Reiki practitioners also use essential oils, crystals, and other alternative therapies to aid healing.

Essential oils

I was unfamiliar with essential oils until two years ago after I had my second baby. At that time I experienced firsthand the benefit of using essential oils when I was given a bottle of bergamot. I had a stressful pregnancy followed by a difficult C-section recovery, and I was feeling physically and emotionally exhausted.

I felt uplifted the moment I smelled bergamot. I can't fully describe it, but the scent gave me an immediate sense of emotional relief. I didn't know then that the nerve endings in our nose pick up the various organic compounds of the oil and send them immediately to the limbic system of the brain, which begins to use them for therapeutic function. The limbic system supports various functions, including emotion, behavior, motivation, and long-term memory.

Essential oils are the botanical extracts of plant leaves, the life force of plants. They can be applied:

1. Externally by massaging them into the skin.

2. Diffused into the air (this being strictly aromatherapy). Aromatherapy is a therapy that uses essential oils to aid healing of physical imbalances as well as emotional disorders such as stress and anxiety. Aromatherapy is often used in conjunction with other holistic treatments like massage therapy, acu-puncture, or reflexology, although many people use them for personal use in their own homes.

3. Taken internally, only when specifically stated on the label, as a dietary supplement, or as prescribed by a qualified practitioner. Be careful when ingesting essential oils; knowledge and expertise is necessary for safe practice.

There is a vast amount of free content on the Internet regarding essential oils. Many books show you how to use them, and many studies have been done regarding their effectiveness. I believe they work because I have experienced physical and emotional relief firsthand, but here are listed a couple of issues that I have with their commercial use:

1. Essential oils are not the "be all and end all" they are promoted to be. With their increased popularity, there are a lot of people with few or no health qualifications who promote and sell them. They make healing claims for major illnesses that although they might be true, the promoters and sellers probably don't have the whole picture of the person who was healed, such as what other therapies they were receiving or how long they had experienced the issue for.

2. Essential oils don't work for everybody and you should never delay seeking your physician's advice while waiting to see if the oils are helping you. Essential oils are wonderful, but no two people are alike; what works for somebody else might not work for you.

Before buying any essential oils, please note the following:

- The market, particularly health shops and some spas, is flooded with impure essential oils that are either treated with chemicals or have chemical additives (such as perfumes). As a general rule, the cheaper the oil, the worse the quality and the worse it is for you.

- Read the label; it should only contain one ingredient: the essential oil. Sometimes distributors and corporations dilute the oil with a "carrier" oil, like coconut oil. This might be okay, but bear in mind that doing this will dilute the potency of the essential oil. This might have been done intentionally if the oil is strong, but the manufacturer could also have done it to sell it more cheaply, and not all carrier oils are good for you. Low quality carrier oils can be hazardous.

- The bottle should always list the botanical (Latin) name of the oil because there are many types of "lavender" oil. Lavender oils include: True lavender (*Lavandula angustifolia*), Spanish lavender (*Lavandula stoechas*), spike lavender (*Lavandula latifolia*), and lavandin (*Lavandula x intermedia*). If it just says "lavender" oil, you don't know what you are getting.

- Be wary of labels that read "100% certified pure," or "Pure therapeutic grade," because there is no certification or regulatory agency in the US to back up those claims. They are usually marketing titles and nothing more.

- Check the container. Essential oils need to be kept in dark glass containers because their chemical compounds interact negatively with plastic.

How I use them

Enjoying the scent of essential oils is very personal. Just like the types of food we like or the clothes we wear, we all have different preferences. I have listed below some of my favorites and how I use them, in case you find it useful.

- When I feel down I use bergamot orange (Citrus aurantium bergamia) peel oil. Actually, even when I feel well I also use it. I just smell it straight out of the bottle as often as I want it. Many other essential oils can also help with emotional issues, but bergamot is my favorite.

- I use peppermint (*Mentha piperita*) and eucalyptus (*Eucalyptus radiata*) for many things. If I have a headache or I feel sleepy, I put a bit of peppermint oil across my forehead. I also use eucalyptus mixed with peppermint (or either on its own) on my hands and then I smell them. It wakes me up and keeps me alert.

- I like using mixed oils for diffusing in my room. I use whatever oils I feel that I need the most. I'm mainly driven by how good they smell and how they make me feel, and I also look at blogs and books for inspiration as to what to mix. Some companies also offer bottles with already mixed oils to improve or assist different afflictions; for example, to improve breathing or to sleep better.

- I rub lavender (*Lavandula angustifolia*) oil on my children's feet (occasionally, as needed) to help them sleep; if they have minor afflictions I will also use a variety of oils to help them. Please note: if my children are unwell I always take them to their pediatrician first, who is a conventional doctor, to see what is wrong with them. I always follow their pediatrician's advice, and I use essential oils as a complement.

- I have used frankincense (*Boswellia carterii*) oil successfully to treat a very stubborn nail fungus that was not going away with conventional means. It is also very good for the skin in general.

Many studies have been done (and books published) on the effectiveness of some oils to be used as antibiotics, or to cure serious ailments like cancer.[26] I believe them to be true; however, although I have said it a few times now, please consult your doctor and use your discernment.

Reflexology

Reflexology is based on the idea that there are reflex points on the feet that correspond to every organ, gland, and part of the body. For

---

[26] US National Library of Medicine online 2014 Jun 9. doi: 10.1155/2014/154106 (PMCID: PMC4070586 https://www.ncbi.nlm.nih.gov/pmc/articles/PMC4070586/

example, the head is reflected in our big toe. With fingers and thumbs, the practitioner applies pressure to these points to treat a wide range of stress-related illnesses. The alternating pressure has a stimulating effect on the body. Reflexology improves nerve and blood supply.

Some people use essential oils and rub them on their feet to aid healing, based on reflexology. I do that often with many types of essential oils.

Reflexology helps the body to restore its balance naturally, and when done by a professional reflexologist it is one of my favorite alternative treatments. (Many spas offer reflexology treatments but the therapist just provides a foot massage. That is not reflexology. If you wish to try it you might want to check first the credentials of the reflexologist, or visit the International Institute of Reflexology website[27] for professional practitioners near you.)

◆ ◆ ◆

The opponents of homeopathy and other alternative treatments claim that the only reason why these therapies work is because of the placebo effect. A placebo is a substance, such as a pill or a shot, that doesn't contain any active medicine. The placebo effect (or placebo response) occurs when this neutral treatment improves a person's condition simply because the person has the expectation that it will be helpful.

It is true to some extent, the stronger our belief that a treatment method will work, the better the results. Our mindset is crucial for healing to occur, but so are other genetic and spiritual factors. I'm not convinced that all alternative therapies work because of the placebo effect.

From my own experience, I tried acupuncture to treat exhaustion. A painful C-section recovery following the birth of my daughter, and going back to work four months later proved to be very taxing for me. Everybody said it was "normal" to feel tired when you have a small

---

[27] http://www.reflexology-usa.net/index.html

baby, but a year and a half after delivery I was still ridiculously tired and depressed. My blood work was normal and I was sleeping well, so my doctor wasn't sure what was causing the tiredness or how to treat it.

I was talking about my tiredness one day with a relative who suggested I try acupuncture, as she was finding it very helpful with her condition. I then remembered that a friend of mine told me how she healed from chronic wrist pain by going to an acupuncturist. So I decided to try it, and I'm glad I did. Although I didn't feel cured after the first session, I did feel slightly better. I went back for about another five or six sessions over the next two months and I totally picked up physically. I wouldn't hesitate to see an acupuncturist again if I needed it.

20

Self-Healing Tools

If you want to know what your thoughts were like yesterday,
then check how your body feels today

INDIAN PROVERB

I F YOU ARE concerned about an aspect of your health, there is a lot you can do to self start the healing process. The flu might just require a bit of rest and proper nutrition, while more complicated diagnoses might need further treatment.

A significant proven method to provide relief and self healing to our bodies is utilizing the power of our mind to heal.

The power of the mind to heal

We have seen throughout the book how our mind and our thoughts are very powerful. Our mindset can aid healing much more than we realize. This has been proven in numerous studies of the placebo effect.

As explained earlier, a placebo is a substance, such as a pill or a shot, that doesn't contain any active medicine. The placebo effect occurs when this neutral treatment improves a person's condition simply because the person has the expectation that it will be helpful. Scientists typically use placebos as controls in research studies. This helps them understand how much of a medicine's effects is due to the drug itself, versus how much is due to a participant's expectations or other factors. Expectations about a drug's healing properties might have a more powerful effect than the drug itself. The expectation is a real drug that causes healing.

Numerous studies[28] have been done about the placebo effect. An article published by the American Psychological Association explains how a placebo alters the brain function of people with depression and basically promotes healing, although no medication was actually given.

In 1981, a team of researchers headed by Harvard psychologist Ellen Langer, Ph.D. [29], author of many books including *Counterclockwise: Counter Health and the Power of Possibility*, took two groups of men in their seventies and eighties to an old monastery in New Hampshire to perform the *Counterclockwise* experiment.

Members of the first group stayed for one week and were asked to pretend they were young men, once again living in the 1950s. Members of the second group, who arrived one week later, were told to stay in the present and simply reminisce about that era. Both groups were surrounded by mid-century mementos. Langer wanted to understand the biological impact of "acting as if."

Before and after the experiment, both groups of men took many cognitive and physical tests, and after just one week, there were significant positive changes across the board.

Both groups showed improvements in physical strength, manual dexterity, posture, perception, memory, cognition, taste sensitivity, hearing, and vision – even their performance on intelligence tests had improved. But the men who had acted as if they were actually back in

---

[28] D. Smith, "Placebo Alters Brain Function of People with Depression," Monitor on Psychology, Vol 33 (3) (American Psychological Association, March 2002)

http://www.apa.org/monitor/mar02/placebo.aspx

[29] http://harvardmagazine.com/2010/09/the-mindfulness-chronicles

the 1950s showed significantly more improvement. Those who had impersonated younger men seemed to have bodies that were actually younger.

These results provide evidence that our mind is very powerful and our thoughts can cause a physical response. Meditation, imagining, remembering, and wondering can all have corresponding physical effects. Dr. Langer said that wherever we put the mind, the body will follow. She explained that it is not our physical state that limits us, but our mindset about our own limits and our perceptions that draws the lines in the sand.

The power of our mind can work to our detriment too; self criticism, doubt, and in general mental stress (anger and heavy emotions) can also alter our nervous system by releasing stress hormones which can affect the body in many ways: adjusting our breathing pattern, increasing our blood pressure, or muscle tension, etc.

In order to heal, we need to eliminate the negative and self-sabotaging thought patterns of the subconscious mind. By accessing that deeper mind, we can rewrite any negative beliefs and patterns that are blocking our ability to heal. We saw earlier that a great tool to do this is with affirmations.

As Dr. Langer's study proved, visualization works very well to aid healing too, because visualizing a healthy body and recalling loving memories from the times when we were healthy will transmit healing frequencies all over our bodies. (Also bear in mind that painful, destructive, and distorted memories transmit frequencies that cause illness and disease.)

A great book that describes general healing methods using the mind and visualizations (as well as meditation exercises) is *The Healing Power of Mind: Simple Meditation Exercises for Health, Well-Being, and Enlightenment*, by Tulku Thondup. I particularly like the visualizations for letting go of sadness and the exercise to focus the scattered mind.

If you wish to read more about the placebo effect, or healing with the mind, I also recommend:

- *You Are the Placebo: Making Your Mind Matter*, by Joe Dispenza
- *Mind Over Medicine: Scientific Proof that You Can Heal Yourself*, by Dr. Lissa Rankin

Self care

Apart from using the power of our mind to help our bodies self heal, there are some other things we can do:

1. Get enough sleep. It is essential for the realignment of our energies. While we sleep our body acclimates to the higher, purer vibration that is our real self. Our energy field also rejuvenates itself.

2. Drink more water, even when you are not thirsty. Studies[30] conducted at the University of Connecticut's Human Performance Laboratory showed that even mild dehydration can alter a person's energy level and his ability to think clearly. It also causes anger, headaches, fatigue, and difficulty concentrating.

3. Wear crystals. A crystal is part of the highest vibration of the mineral kingdom, and crystals interact with our biology.

4. Use EFT tapping. Definition from the Tapping Solution Foundation:[31] "Tapping is a combination of Ancient Chinese Acupressure and Modern Psychology that works to physically alter your brain, energy system and body all at once. The practice consists of tapping with your fingertips on specific

---

[30] http://jn.nutrition.org/content/early/2011/12/20/jn.111.142000.abstract

https://doi.org/10.1017/S0007114511002005

[31] http://www.tappingsolutionfoundation.org/howdoesitwork/

meridian points while talking through traumatic memories and a wide range of emotions."

The combination of tapping the energy meridians and voicing positive statements works to heal emotional blocks. If you wish to learn more about tapping, please read *The Tapping Solution: A Revolutionary System for Stress-Free Living* by Nick Ortner, or *The EFT Manual* by Gary Craig. There are also many free online resources and probably at your local library.

5. Unclutter your house and your life (see Chapters 16 and 25). Let go of stuff and relationships that are no longer serving you. Surround yourself with beautiful, uplifting things and people. The energy field of people, places, things, and your own home can amplify and add to your personal energy.

6. Go outside more and get more sunlight, which contains UV light. When sunlight is absorbed through the skin it produces Vitamin D, promoting the production of serotonin.

Doreen Virtue, in her book *Angel Medicine: How to Heal the Body and Mind with the Help of the Angels*, explains over 10 reasons why sunlight is so important for healing. For example, Vitamin D depletion can be dangerous; low exposure has been linked to cancer; and sunlight increases mental and physical performance.

I had an idea that the sun was an important aspect for our well-being, and Virtue certainly explains it thoroughly. But what I really liked in her "Sunshine" chapter was learning to understand the repercussions of wearing sunglasses, contact lenses, and eyeglasses to our eye's ability to detect sun rays. It appears that these types of eye wear cause the brain to not realize the extent of sun exposure we are getting, so it doesn't secrete as much melatonin as it would in full sunlight (melatonin makes us tan and provides natural sun protection). Basically, she says that our body doesn't realize it is getting exposure to sunlight so the body doesn't produce its natural defenses that enable it to prevent sunburn.

Biologically, we are meant to be exposed to sunlight for health and happiness, but she warns us as well to be in the sun in moderation (morning or late afternoon).

7. Get a massage. One particular study focused on pregnant women: Those who received massages twice a week from their partner boosted their serotonin levels by 30%.

8. Get active. Walk more. Do some exercise.

9. Use natural products.

Natural products won't heal, but they can prevent you from getting ill if you are currently using products that contain an excessive amount of chemicals. Toxic chemicals are everywhere (in our food, personal care products, and cleaning products), but we can limit our exposure to them with just a little knowledge on our part.

The skin is the largest organ in the body, and it absorbs a lot of the products we put on it. We can see this at work with effective treatments like hormone replacement therapy or nicotine patches. Also, the reason essential oils that we put on the bottom of our feet could have healing effects is that the oil compounds pass through the skin, then into the capillaries, and finally into the bloodstream.

Because of the ability of our skin to absorb what we put on it we need to be careful what products we use. For example, most sunscreens are harmful. Environmental Working Group (EWG) research[32] reveals that the chemicals commonly used in sunscreens may interfere with thyroid and other hormone processes in the body. The EWG and Consumer Reports have warned consumers against using many types of conventional sunscreens; they offer a false sense of security regarding sun protection and may do more harm than good. Mineral sunscreens, without sunscreen chemicals, are a good alternative option.

---

[32] http://www.ewg.org/sunscreen/report/skin-cancer-on-the-rise/

Most candles are not good either. Generally, scented candles are a source of indoor air pollution and they emit chemicals that are considered dangerous. Most candles contain:

- Paraffin wax, which, when burned, creates carcinogens such as benzene and toluene. Paraffin is the final byproduct in the petroleum refining chain.
- Wicks, that in some cases contain heavy metals like lead, which in turn create air concentrations of lead above the US Environmental Protection Agency (EPA) recommended thresholds.
- Artificial scents and dyes, which when burned, also release additional chemicals.

In 2001, EPA concluded[33] that burning paraffin candles emits harmful amounts of toxins in the air.

Extracted from the report:

When candles are burned, they emit trace amounts of organic chemicals, including acetaldehyde, formaldehyde, acrolein, and naphthalene (Lau et al., 1997). However, the primary constituent of public health concern in candle emissions is lead. Metal was originally put in wicks to keep the wick standing straight when the surrounding wax begins to melt. The metal prevents the wick from falling over and extinguishing itself as soon as the wax fails to support it. The US candle manufacturing industry voluntarily agreed to cease production of lead-containing candles in 1974, once it was shown that burning lead-wick candles resulted in increased lead concentrations in indoor air (Sobel et al., 2000b). Unfortunately, despite the voluntary ban, lead wick candles can still be found on the market.

---

[33] https://cfpub.epa.gov/si/si_public_record_report.cfm?dirEntryId=20899

https://nepis.epa.gov/Exe/ZyPDF.cgi?Dockey=P1009BZL.txt

A similar issue arises with incense:

> Exposure to incense smoke has been linked with several illnesses, and certain brands of incense also contain chemicals suspected of causing skin irritation. Several studies indicated links between exposure to incense smoke and health effects, including cancers and contact dermatitis. A few studies indicated possible mutagenic and genotoxic effects.

The alternative to toxic candles is 100 percent beeswax candles with cotton wicks. You can find them in the resources[34] section at Green America© website (a not-for-profit organization that aims to create a socially just and environmentally sustainable society). Beeswax can cost as much as six times the price of paraffin, so many candle manufacturers blend paraffin with their beeswax to cut costs. Be sure your candles say 100 percent beeswax or 100 percent vegetable-based waxes on the label.

Instead of candles, you can also use a diffuser with essential oils, which has the added bonus of potentially assisting healing.

10. Last but not least as a self-healing tool, food is a great physical source of energy that is usually ignored in the role of healing, or relegated to an afterthought. In the next chapter we take a look at healing with nutrition.

---

[34] http://www.greenamerica.org/livinggreen/candles.cfm

21

Healing with Nutrition

The food you eat can be either the safest and most
powerful form of medicine or the slowest form of poison

ANN WIGMORE

THE IMPORTANCE OF a nutritious diet is often overlooked. Energy is necessary to the healing process as our bodies need energy to fulfill a myriad of processes.

The main purpose of this chapter is to emphasize the importance of providing our bodies with adequate nutrients, and at the same time to raise awareness about what goes in our foods, by looking at the importance of reading food labels and eating organic food.

One of the biggest issues today is the quality, origin, and amount of processing in the food we eat. Our ancestors used to eat what was naturally available within their region. They ate whole, fresh, generally balanced meals with organically grown foods that were seasonal and local. Today, we eat frozen fruit flown across the Atlantic or a "good for you" ready packaged meal without fully understanding the implications for our body's ability to heal.

The life force in food

In Chapter 17, we saw how Dr. Burr recorded the existence of an energy field in all living things. His findings are particularly relevant in the context of the food we eat.

Live plants and cut plants don't have the same type of energy field; the more time that elapses from the moment of cutting, the more the field of the cut plant changes, until the field eventually disappears.

Frozen foods, even when packaged in their original form (plain frozen fruits or vegetables, for example) are not ideal because the life force in them diminishes. When food is frozen, the cells in the water of those foods burst, which is the reason why untreated vegetables are mushy and limp when thawed. For this reason, canned and frozen foods might contain all the nutrients present in fresh food, but they are not as healthy.

Poor diet and excessive stress can deplete the body's energy reserves very quickly. If we have major surgery and subsequently we eat nutrient deficient foods, it is going to take much longer for our body to repair itself.

Food provides us with energy, plays a critical role in the regulation of numerous body processes, and can act as natural protectors against disease, by:

- Detoxifying and eliminating toxins.
- Balancing blood pressure and cholesterol levels, and assisting with digestion and elimination of waste.
- Balancing blood sugar levels. Diabetes and weight gain are tied to poor insulin response and other hormonal changes. Unregulated sugar levels can lead to increased cravings, fatigue, crankiness, and a number of hormonal issues.
- Controlling internal inflammation in the body, which is the root of many diseases. Symptoms of inflammation include fatigue, being overweight, aches and pains, allergies or infections, and a diagnosed autoimmune disease.

When the body is lacking something, like proper nutrition in the form of vitamins and minerals, it tries to compensate. The body will try to find an equal alternative for what is lacking, but if it can't find what it needs, it will use a substitute, either a physical alternative, or a symbolic one. (This is one of the reasons people get cravings for things like chalk, dirt, and paint.) This is also the reason why when we eat a meal deficient in nutrients (e.g., fast or junk food) we are hungry a few hours later; our body is still looking for nutrients.

Reading food labels

The best food is always natural, wholesome, one item, non-processed food (meats, vegetables, fruits, etc.) However, it is not always possible or practical to cook from scratch, and also there are some good prepackaged foods (like some types of meats or packaged vegetables).

When reading food labels, keep in mind the following:

1. The ingredients appear on the food label in order of quantity; the ingredient that weighs the most is listed first, and the one that weighs the least is listed last, from most to least. For example, breakfast cereals are usually very unhealthy. They may contain whole wheat listed first and then sugar or high fructose corn syrup second, because most cereals have huge amounts of sugars. Always aim for a short ingredients list. A common rule of thumb is to look for food with no more than five ingredients. If the ingredients list is longer than a couple of lines, then the product is highly processed.

2. Be aware of sugar in disguise and labels that claim, "No added sugar," which doesn't mean it's healthy, or that it doesn't have sugar substitutes. Usually sugar is not labeled as such; it might go by different names: 1) Syrups, like high fructose corn syrup, brown rice syrup, maple syrup, corn syrup, fruit syrup, golden syrup; 2) Sugars finishing in "ose," like dextrose, fructose, glucose, sucrose, lactose, maltose; 3) Other sugars like brown sugar, inverted sugar, raw sugar, agave nectar, fruit juice

concentrate, molasses, monosaccharides, disaccharides, mannitol, sorbitol, and xylitol. Always look at the ingredients list, not just the nutritional label.

3. Also, there is a difference between naturally found sugar (in fruits, milk, etc.) and added sugar. For example; in milk, the nutritional label might say sugar: 11 grams per serving, but sugar is not listed in the ingredients list as an *added* ingredient.

4. Don't believe everything you read on the front of the package. The word *organic* on a package label doesn't mean it's necessarily a healthy food. Be wary also of any products with big claims like "All Natural," which might still contain questionable ingredients, or "Fat Free," which usually means there are a lot of additives or other substitutes just to make it less calorific, but not more nutritional. I like this example from the *Health and Healing* book by Annemarie Colbin: "*Fat Free Mayonnaise* is an oxymoron, since real mayonnaise is just eggs and oil. A clear example that you are just buying junk food."

5. Packaged processed foods (prepared and "fortified" meals), replacement shakes, most "healthy" snack bars, fast or fried food, and some canned foods are all deficient or void in vitamins and minerals, and they are packed with synthetic ingredients and preservatives that result in a partial or fully depleted food energy field. As a rule of thumb, the cheaper the "meal" or snack, the cheaper and nastier the ingredients. You won't see broccoli in the super market aisle with a label that says "packed with vitamin A, B1, B6, E, and minerals; magnesium, zinc, calcium, iron, niacin and selenium," which it has, but most packaged foods that are full of sugar, salt, preservatives, and colorants will most likely have a big label that says how many vitamins and minerals have been added to the package, trying to lure us into thinking the meal is good for us. It is not. It is always best to eat our food in its original form (whole grains and whole foods).

6. Be aware of any ingredients you don't understand. If you have never heard of it, or you can't pronounce it, it is probably not "food." Food additives, sugar, colorants, and the like have been added to our foods to create addiction and increase the profit of corporations, not our health.

7. Some ingredients are toxic and dangerous for our bodies. For example, artificial color Red No. 3 – Erythorosine, is banned in cosmetics but is still allowed in food.[35] You can find more about this in Vani Hari's website.[36] Hari (the Food Babe) teaches people how to make the right purchasing decisions at the grocery store and how to live an organic lifestyle.

8. Last but not least, diet sodas and many "light" or "natural" drinks are laden with very unhealthy ingredients. Make sure to read those labels too, and avoid all sweeteners. Dr. Josh Axe has written various articles about what diet sodas and sweeteners do to our bodies.[37] They may cause depression, kidney damage, and cardiovascular disease among other issues. Dr. Axe is a board certified doctor of natural medicine, a doctor of chiropractic, and a clinical nutritionist. His website[38] is one of the top 10 most visited natural health websites in the world and it offers a large amount of free content around nutrition, natural medicine, fitness, healthy recipes, home remedies, and trending health news.

---

[35] 5 Ingredients That Should Have Never Been Approved by the FDA – Are you Eating Them?

http://foodbabe.com/2015/01/08/5-ingredients-that-should-have-never-been-approved-by-the-fda-are-you-eating-them/

[36] http://foodbabe.com

[37] https://draxe.com/sweet-addiction-artificial-sweeteners-not-so-sweet-after-all/

https://draxe.com/is-diet-soda-bad-for-you/

[38] https://draxe.com

Organic whole foods are best

From a vibrational energy stand point, there is a reason organic stuff (particularly food) is better. Organic foods are produced without the employment of chemically formulated fertilizers, growth stimulants, antibiotics, or pesticides.

Pesticides that are sprayed all over fruits and vegetables decrease the vibrational rate of the produce to below that which sustains life. The more pesticides in foods, the more the energy field of the food is distorted and weakened.

The quality of the meat we eat is not much better. The beef and chicken industry is ruthless. Animals are being kept in terrible conditions, in minimal, enclosed spaces with no chance of exercise. They are fed food deficient in nutrients and full of pesticides, fungicides, and herbicides. These animals are given hormones and antibiotics to help them through the ordeal so they can grow older in order to be killed and sold at the highest profit possible. Antibiotics, drugs, and growth hormones are passed directly into meat and dairy products. Farmed fish poses a similar issue with the type of diet they are fed.

Animals have not always been treated this way. Native American people knew that animals deserve as much respect as human beings. They treated all animals as equals. In ceremonies, they would ask for permission to receive the nourishment from the animals about to be hunted and killed.

Between the pesticides in our foods, and the poor treatment and diets of animals, we are bombarded by chemicals that contribute to a range of diseases. Although we might not be consciously aware of this, all of the food we eat carries its own frequency and affects our nervous system. Our body resonates with some food and tenses with others.

Try to eat organic food and ethically raised meat whenever possible and affordable. Local produce from local farmers is probably the best quality food you can find, although it might not always be accredited as "organic" (it is quite expensive for small farmers to obtain the "organic" accreditation, although their produce might be free of pesticides).

There are two lists on the EWG website that lists which foods contain the highest amount of pesticides ("dirty dozen"),[39] and which ones the least ("clean fifteen").[40] If you can't afford to buy all of your produce organic, you might want to ensure you buy organic the items listed in the "dirty dozen" foods (which contain the highest amount of pesticides).

For 2016, the worst produce with the highest amount of pesticides were, in order (highest first): strawberries, apples, nectarines, peaches, celery, grapes, cherries, spinach, tomatoes, sweet bell peppers, cherry tomatoes, cucumbers, hot peppers, and kale/collard greens.

The cleanest foods were, in this order: avocados, sweet corn, pineapples, cabbage, sweet peas (frozen), onions, asparagus, mangos, papayas, kiwi, eggplant, honeydew, lemon, grapefruit, cantaloupe, and cauliflower.

The risks of eating dietary supplements

We assume dietary supplements, such as vitamins and minerals, herbs, sport nutrition, and weight management supplements are safe because they are often described as natural, but they can cause harm both directly – through drug interactions and because they may have dangerous ingredients – and indirectly, by delaying conventional care. There are also some other dangers.

We believe we can trust the advice of some individuals and corporations because they have been selling them for a long time, like in a gym or a health shop, or we self-prescribe what we need by reading the label. Please consider the following:

1. Some supplements are not as "pure" as the seller or the label claims them to be. A number of well-known toxins have been

---

found in herbal preparations, sometimes resulting in significant human injury.

Dr. Pieter Cohen, an assistant professor at Harvard Medical School and expert on the dietary supplement industry, found his patients started developing mysterious symptoms. One woman went in with palpitations, sweating, and anxiety, but also feeling very tired. Another was rushed to the emergency room with kidney failure, and one man lost his job after his urine tested positive for amphetamines. Cohen realized his patients were all taking weight loss pills known as rainbow diet pills. He then sent the capsules off to a private lab for testing. The tests revealed amphetamines, thyroid hormones, diuretics, benzo-diazepines (tranquilizers), and antidepressants.

Cohen has written numerous articles.[41] If you want to read more about Cohen's work you can visit *The Harvard Clinical and Translational Science Center*, and look under Harvard Catalyst profiles.[42]

2. Sellers aren't required to do research studies in people to prove that a dietary supplement is safe. Supplements, like drugs, can also have side effects, and you can overdose on vitamins and minerals.

3. Taking dietary pills might pose a risk to special populations: children, elderly, pregnant women, people undergoing surgery, or people with impaired organ or immunologic function. Even if you don't fall into any of the above groups, always seek your doctor's advice to determine if you need to take any pills. Self medicating is dangerous. A study[43] published in the *British Medical Journal* revealed that additional calcium poises an

---

[41] http://harvardpublichealthreview.org/how-americas-flawed-supplement-law-creates-the-mirage-of-weight-loss-cures/

[42] https://connects.catalyst.harvard.edu/profiles/display/person/21925

[43] BMJ Publishing Group website: BMJ 2011;342: d2040. Published 19 April 2011.

http://www.bmj.com/content/342/bmj.d2040.full

increase in heart risk. Another study found that Vitamin E, which was originally thought to protect the heart, was later discovered to increase the risk for bleeding strokes.

The bottom line is, seek your doctor's advice, read the ingredients list, and take supplements only as prescribed. If you don't understand an ingredient, research it, and be satisfied that you know what you are taking into your body.

Microwaves

I have read differing points of view on whether microwaves are good or bad for you, but overall there seems to be a big concern around them; they alter the field of the foods being cooked.

Paul Pitchford, in *Healing with Whole Foods: Asian Traditions and Modern Nutrition* writes that microwave cooking seems to damage the molecular integrity of the food, diminishing the subtle *qi* (life force). He says that experiments reported in the British medical journal *The Lancet*, on December 9, 1989, demonstrate that microwave cooking alters food enough to cause, upon ingestion, "structural, functional, and immunological changes" in the body. The report further states that microwaves transform the amino acid L-proline into D-proline, a proven toxin to the nervous system, liver, and kidneys.

Also, an article called *The Hidden Hazards of Microwave Cooking*,[44] by Anthony Wayne and Lawrence Newell, published in *Health-Science*, shows evidence that microwave cooking is not natural, nor healthy, and is far more dangerous to the human body than anyone could imagine. It is very well researched and eye opening.

---

[44] https://www.health-science.com/microwave_hazards.html

A word of caution

I have read many books and articles that assert how some diets can cure illnesses. Some books recommend a vegan or raw plant based diet as a sole or complementary therapy. Other books claim that if you have a specific disease (for example, some types of blood cancers), you would benefit from eating red meat. There are a lot of mixed messages and confusing information out there.

When we are sick, we are more vulnerable to believe that some treatment is going to help us. Please do not blindly follow anybody or any specific health system. We are not all the same, and the same disease can be caused by different reasons.

Follow your doctor's directions and decide what is best for you. Some diets can do more harm than good, particularly when you are asked to eliminate entire food groups like meat or fruit.

Annemarie Colbin, in her book *Food and Healing,* has a very good point. She says that good food will nourish us without causing stress, allowing our immune system to spend its energy in healing. Therefore, because our immune system can concentrate on other things, some diets will have healing effects. I have also read in other books that fasting can also be a great healer for the same reason (our body can concentrate on repairing itself instead of spending time and energy with digestion and dealing with the stress of handling chemicals and poor nutritional foods).

Colbin also says that often it is not just what we eat, but also what we don't eat, that helps us become healthy again. She gives the example that a diet free of nuts, nut butters, soda pop, fried foods, mayonnaise, and dairy products does not "cure" acne; it just doesn't cause acne, and therefore the body returns to normal and the acne disappears.

◆ ◆ ◆

One last thing. Adequate nutrition is very important, but try not to become a food fanatic. I believe that the constant fear of eating the wrong things can be worse than eating a simple cupcake. In this chapter I've highlighted some issues so the next time you shop you might make better informed choices.

In the next chapters 22 through 24 we will continue to attempt to cover all aspects of healing and taking care of our physical body. I have done some research and I have read some wonderful books about dieting, weight loss, and exercise that I wish to share. I believe it is important to understand why diets don't work and how we can lose weight in order to be at peace with every aspect of our lives; physically, mentally, and emotionally.

22

Why Diets Don't Work

I have been on a diet for two weeks, and all I have lost is two weeks

TOTIE FIELDS

AS WE SAW in the previous chapter, there is a lot of nutritional and medicinal value when we eat the right food and get the right nutrients in our bodies. This chapter is going to deal with the issue of dieting in the context of restricting oneself to small amounts, or special amounts and types of food to lose weight.

If we honestly ask ourselves what we need to do to lose weight, we will probably come up with a sensible answer, such as cutting down on junk food and alcohol, and doing some daily exercise. So if it is so simple, why is it so hard to lose weight?

As a society we have become accustomed to using outside resources to guide us about what to eat, how much, and when. We trust them because so far we haven't been successful using our own strategies to lose weight. There is always, of course, validity in consulting professionals, and many dietitians offer invaluable help and knowledge to those who need it. However, the problem is that many dieting companies are trying to profit at the expense of what is good for us, and without treating the real issue in some cases; for example, overeating due to stress and emotional problems.

Before I had my first child I was slim, although I wasn't happy with the way I looked; I wanted to be thinner. Looking back at the clothes I used to wear they were small (US size 6), so I'm not sure what I was seeing in the mirror, but it was not my idea of perfection.

After having my first son, I continued to eat the same way I did before getting pregnant, but to my horror I was not losing all the extra weight. I assumed it would take time, but time passed and I was still carrying the extra weight. About a year after I had him I started to diet, and at that point I started to have a very unhealthy relationship with food. Food became my main preoccupation and obsession, while up to that point it had never affected me that much. I had done the occasional diet in my twenties, but I never really worried about it to that extent. Since I had my first child, every time I started a new diet I would lose weight, only to gain it again within a short period of time.

Many years later, I had my second child; at this point it was my fourth pregnancy as I had previously lost two babies.

The first time my OBGYN told me my baby's heart had stopped beating I cried for hours (and weeks); I was utterly devastated. Subsequently, I lost another baby, and by the time I got pregnant for the fourth time, and despite my best efforts to be positive and happy about it, I was terribly worried about losing my baby again.

During the last pregnancy I started to obsess over how often I could feel the baby kicking, and the OBGYN ultrasound checkups were a nightmare. Instead of looking forward to seeing my baby, I would be holding my breath until I could hear the baby's heartbeat. I was given plenty of reassurances that she was okay, but I would leave the doctor's office and eat. I was fully aware of what I was doing, thinking that I shouldn't be eating so much. But I did it anyway. I just felt the urge to eat, and I thought I could deal with the fat body later. In my last pregnancy I ate way more than I ever did with my first one; and subsequently, I put on a lot more weight.

The reason I tell you my story is because now I have the experience of going on many diets (unsuccessfully) and I can testify to the fact that if losing weight was as simple as eating the right food, the diet industry wouldn't be worth billions of dollars.

For the past eight years I have tried many diets and I have read many diet books. Today, I don't diet, and I have no intentions of ever going on a diet again. I hope that all the information that I have gathered helps you to understand why dieting might not be working for you and what you can do to lose weight.

We can't force our body to diet

Our bodies will tell us when to eat, what to eat, and how much, and this will change on a regular basis. We move out of trust with our body when we get caught up in dieting.

The moment we try to change the body, the body resists. It is a primary survival mechanism; if we cut down the amount of food we give it, the first thing it does when it feels threatened is to store fat. It is not a case of lacking will power, it is the body's intelligence kicking in, doing what it is supposed to be doing, balancing itself and conserving energy at all costs.

Deepak Chopra, in his book, *Quantum Healing, Exploring the Frontiers of Mind/Body Medicine* explains:

Unless some degree of control is gained at a very deep level, obese people can spend their whole lives forcing themselves to diet, a self-defeating tactic that only makes the mental distortion worse. The loss of 10 pounds is registered in their brain as famine, and the next time food is offered, the brain will not stop until 15 pounds is put back on, adding an extra five as a safety margin against the next famine. Obese people have been known to gain weight on diets where no extra calories are offered beyond the bare minimum to sustain metabolism. The reason for this is that the brain can actually alter the metabolism in such a way that the calories are stored as fat instead of being burned up as fuel.

It has been proven that people on a diet tend to feel hungrier, and it is not a will power problem; it is a normal expected hormonal response.

In the Minnesota Starvation Experiment, Dr. Ancel Keys documented the effect of "semi-starvation neurosis." The full report and results from the Minnesota Starvation Experiment was published by the University of Minnesota Press in 1950, in a two-volume, 1,385-page text called *The Biology of Human Starvation*. The study intended to understand the physical and psychological effects of severe and prolonged dietary restriction. Thirty-six men were given a diet that contained approximately 3,200 calories a day for the first three months, then 1,600 calories a day for the following six months. (Many diets today don't offer as many calories.)

The findings of this experiment can be summarized as follows:

- Prolonged semi-starvation produced significant increases in depression, hysteria, and hypochondriasis. Most of the participants experienced periods of severe emotional distress and depression.
- The act of restricting food and the constant hunger made food "the most important thing in one's life," said one of the participants. Participants exhibited extreme preoccupation with food, during both the starvation period and the rehabilitation phase. They obsessed and dreamed about food. Men began to obsessively collect food recipes. Interest in anything else diminished.
- Sexual interest was drastically reduced, and the volunteers showed signs of social withdrawal and isolation.
- The participants reported a decline in concentration, comprehension, and judgment capabilities.

The two most remarkable effects of this experiment I wish to highlight are:

- In the beginning, all participants lost a lot of weight. In the first 12 weeks they averaged a loss of a pound a week, but in the subsequent 12 weeks they only averaged a loss of a quarter of a pound a week. That is because their bodies' survival mechanisms kicked in. The study showed a marked decline in each participant's basal metabolic rate (the energy required by the body in a state of rest), and reduced body temperature, respiration, and heart rate. When the body feels threatened, it will try to conserve energy at all costs by slowing the metabolism and increasing hunger and fat storage. When we try to lose weight, hitting plateaus is seen as a big inconvenience, yet it is a perfect mechanism of survival, otherwise, anorexics would be dead within two months.

- When the men were allowed to eat freely again, they had insatiable appetites, yet never felt full. Even five months later, some continued to have dysfunctional eating, although most were finally regaining some normalization of their eating.

In *The Obesity Code: Unlocking the Secrets of Weight Loss,* Jason Fung, MD, explains that obesity is not about calories, or fat grams, or exercise, but about hormones, and that when insulin levels run too high for too long we develop "insulin resistance," which can make us fat. Insulin is a hormone that regulates our metabolism.

Dr. Fung believes there is a "set point" for body weight and fatness. When we try to diet, our weight drops below our body's set weight and our body naturally activates a compensatory mechanism to raise it (such as our metabolism shuts down and our body temperature and heart rate drops in an effort to conserve energy). Fung says this is the reason dieters are usually cold, hungry, grumpy, and depressed, and that the problem with obesity is that the set point is too high.

To correct the hormonal imbalance, Dr. Fung believes that we need to change not only what we eat, but when we eat, by practicing intermittent fasting. He writes about fasting traditions in human history and how fasting affects hormones.

I can't say if his dietary and lifestyle recommendations for weight loss work because I haven't tried them. (Because I believe my overeating issues are primarily emotionally driven and I don't have a hormonal issue, but I believe these two issues often co-exist). I really enjoyed reading his book and learning a number of things: how stress contributes to weight gain, why fat doesn't make you fat, what drives yo-yo dieting, the reason behind obesity and weight loss, and much more. I highly recommend *The Obesity Code*.

The bottom line is, we can't force our bodies to diet and be a specific weight and size that we have in mind. The body will always seek to balance itself.

We are not all the same

We are not the same, and we all view food with different eyes. We can't standardize all diet rules out there as if we are identical beings. We are not. A person might thrive on a raw or vegan diet, while another one might get sick following it. Years ago I tried to become vegetarian because I sincerely thought it was the healthy, ethical, and environmentally responsible way to live. But my body didn't agree. I felt sick, weak, and tired. To this day I need meat to function properly although the quantities I need vary from week to week.

Some specific diets might work for the person who came up with them, because the type of foods, frequency, and quantities of what they ate might have been perfect for their body requirements and their consciousness at the time, and therefore they lost weight (and probably kept it off too). We need to leave general rules and everybody else out of the equation. It doesn't matter how much *they* eat, what *they* weigh, exercise, or not. *They* are not *you*.

The reason for being overweight might be different in each person. It is very different to be gaining weight out of emotional stress, or sleep deprivation, versus gaining it simply because of excessive consumption of nutrient deprived (junk) food. We will need to handle how to lose weight in different ways. In the same way that identical medical treatment doesn't work for two people with the same diagnosis, the same diet will not work for everybody.

There is no consensus – diet advice is too confusing

Since I started dieting eight years ago I have come across many diets. I first started to diet following a low fat diet, which has now been rightly trashed as not being healthy. Then I learned of some odd diets that encouraged me to consume only soup, or juice, or take shakes, or pills for long periods of time; even to inject hormones. Luckily, I didn't do many of these. Then I followed a variety of other diets, a mix of "don't eat carbs", and "avoid all sugar, gluten, dairy" – until in the end I felt there wasn't much left to eat. Regardless of the type of diet I was on, I always felt deprived and miserable.

I also tried eating everything I wanted but restricted to counting calories and points. Nothing lasted long term for me. Some diets also had strong views about how often we should eat each day and the portion size. "Never eat snacks," or "Snack once or twice a day to raise your metabolism"; "Have a treat each week," or "Never ever have treats." Most diet books provide all sorts of studies to back up their claims, and "before" and "after" pictures. So, who is right?

They are all right *and* wrong. As I mentioned earlier, we are not all the same, and what works for one person will not necessarily work for another one. In some cases, even what might work for somebody in the short term is not sustainable or healthy in the longer term, so we need to be careful with some diets.

I struggled with the low carb diet the most. Not only did I want to eat the usually forbidden foods (like a piece of chocolate cake), I also wanted fruit, rice, pasta, sweet potatoes, and oat meal – all normal foods that I was restricting because I wanted to lose weight.

I dislike all the rules because I feel we are over complicating life. I understand there is an obesity epidemic, but some of the dietary restrictions are way too extreme; advice such as: "Don't eat too many carrots or fruit because they are high in carbs" (or because of their sugar content), or "Count your portions even when eating vegetables." People are not obese because they overeat fruit and vegetables.

I understand some people say that too much fruit can worsen a condition called candida. But if you have a medical condition you should be following your doctor's advice anyway, so if your doctor restricts or completely forbids fruit, I'm not going to dispute that. But I would not restrict fruits and vegetables in a healthy individual.

Fruits have many great nutritional qualities like being high in fiber and rich in water, minerals, and B-vitamins; they are also full of antioxidants and many substances that have been shown to fight cancer, improve mood and energy, and generally support overall health and wellness. You will not be doing your body any favors by avoiding fruit.

Dan Buettner, bestselling author and National Geographic fellow, reveals, in *The Blue Zone Solution: Eating and Living Like the World's Healthiest People,* what the longest lived people have eaten over the past 100 years. He wanted to locate places that had not only a high concentration of 100 year olds, but also clusters of people who had grown old without diseases such as heart problems, obesity, cancer, or diabetes.

He discovered five blue zones around the world, one of which was in Ikaria (Greece), where they followed a Mediterranean diet. Since I love coffee, I read with interest that one of the key staples in their diet was coffee, two or three cups a day of Turkish style Ikarian coffee. (Note: the lattes and processed coffees currently served in coffee chains with all types of sweeteners and additives are not what the Ikarians consumed nor what I would call a traditional cup of coffee.)

I have read mixed reports as to whether coffee is good for you or not. Most of the books I have read cite other studies to support or discourage the consumption of coffee, and I haven't found any consensus on the topic. The fact that a region in the world drinks coffee with no ill effects doesn't make it right for you either, but I have quoted this example to highlight my point that there is no universal right or wrong when it comes to the right diet.

Interestingly, Buettner also said that none of the 253 lively centenarians he met ever went on a diet, joined a gym, or took supplements. To various degrees and amounts they also ate carbs (including rice, breads, fruits, and sweet potatoes), and meat, fish, eggs, and dairy.

His book reminded me of the Asian paradox. The no-carb diet is very popular at the moment, but if you think about obesity, do Asians come to mind? White rice is their main food staple.

The influence of our thoughts when dieting

We could be following the best diet in the world and still not produce the weight loss we want. Let's see how our thoughts make all the difference. In the following study[45], Dr. Alia Crum proved how our bodies will metabolize the same meal quite differently in response to our unique thoughts.

Dr. Crum, who has a Ph.D. in Clinical Psychology from Yale University, conducted a study called *Mind over milkshakes: Mindsets, not just nutrients, determine ghrelin response,* to try to determine how mindset can affect an individual's appetite, and how it could affect the production of a gut peptide called ghrelin (which is involved in the feeling of satisfaction after eating). Ghrelin levels are supposed to rise when the body needs food and fall proportionally as the body consumes calories, telling the brain the body is no longer hungry and doesn't need more food.

On two separate occasions, 46 participants consumed a 380-calorie milkshake under the pretense that it was either a 620-calorie "indulgent" shake or a 140-calorie "sensible" shake. Ghrelin was measured via intravenous blood samples at three time points: baseline (20 min), anticipatory (60 min), and post-consumption (90 min). The

---

[45] A. Crum, "Mind over milkshakes: Mindsets, Not Just Nutrients, Determine Ghrelin Response."

Journal Health Psychology (2011, Vol. 30, No. 4, 424 -429).

https://www.ncbi.nlm.nih.gov/pubmed/21574706

data showed that ghrelin levels changed depending on how many calories participants were told they were consuming, not how many they actually consumed. Those who were given the "Indulgence" labelled shakes reported greater satiety and a dramatic drop in ghrelin – about three times the drop as those who thought they were drinking a low-calorie shake.

Basically, the results prove that the mindset of indulgence produced a dramatically steeper decline in ghrelin after consuming the shake, whereas the mindset of sensibility produced a relatively flat ghrelin response. Participants' satiety was consistent with what they believed they were consuming, rather than the actual nutritional value of what they consumed. In other words, participants felt fuller when they thought they were drinking a high calorie drink, and didn't feel as full when they thought they were consuming a light drink. However, both drinks had the same amount of calories.

Let's think about the implications of this study. How many times have you said, "I should be eating salad instead of this?" I used to think that diet food (and dieting in general) was never filling enough, so it didn't matter if the food I was eating had enough calories to sustain me; I thought I was not eating enough and my body was reacting accordingly. I was hungry all the time.

This study is fascinating and frustrating, since I didn't know this at that time when I was dieting to no end.

This study simplifies why diets don't work. Our mindset about dieting is one of the keys to success, but it is often overlooked. Our emotional health is also another key to success.

◆ ◆ ◆

On a spiritual note, our soul wants to experience growth and freedom, not obsess over anything in life, including our weight and food. Diets have the opposite effect. They restrict what we can eat, how, and when.

Our excessive preoccupation with the size of our body might be one of our life lessons to overcome. The obsession with food, calories, and dieting triggers too many food thoughts, and what consumes our mind controls our life.

It is uncommon to hear a naturally thin person constantly talk or think about food, or feel guilty about their choices. They eat whenever they are hungry and whatever they want. It might be the case that our life lesson is to let it go and realize that obsessing about the shape of our body is not healthy.

Our soul might be longing for us to acknowledge the fact that our real self is much more than our body, particularly if we feel we always had weight problems.

To conclude, it is good to seek advice and talk to a dietician if that is what you wish to do, but in the end it is best to decide for yourselves what will or will not work for your body. Nobody else will ever be able to pick up the messages your body and intuition are sending you.

23

How to Lose Weight

You have been criticizing yourself for years, and it hasn't worked.
Try approving of yourself and see what happens.

LOUISE L. HAY

MOST OF US are searching for the fast, immediate answer to get us to our weight goal, but the reality is that because we haven't put on weight overnight we can't expect to lose it overnight either. It is likely that one or many of the following scenarios occurred:

- Once upon a time, there was a painful life experience that triggered overeating and the stress continued for a long time. It might still be present.

- We were brought up in a household with poor eating habits, and we continue the same habits – most of the time because we don't know any better.

- We had no emotional trauma, but we started developing small (bad) habits and over time they snowballed into eating more and lower quality food. One drive-thru (or similar easy to get fast food) meal a month became once a week, which became three or four times a week. Or we started a new stressful job and began to drink more alcohol after dinner "to relax." That behavior continued over time, with or without a stressful job.

- We might just like eating good food above our constituent needs, or our body has a propensity issue to be larger (in the same manner that there are "naturally" thin people).

- Over many years of poor eating habits, our body has developed insulin resistance.

- To top it all off, at some point we decided to go on a new diet and we attempted to give up all the "bad" food and habits at once. We said goodbye to sugar, gluten, carbs, soda, caffeine, and alcohol; and, in some cases, fruit and meat too. Nothing, it was all gone, and with the limited types and amounts of food that we were allowed to eat, we had to check and count our portions too.

Giving up all "bad" food and alcohol at once doesn't make sense to me. If we build a bad habit over time, then it is more sensible to lose it overtime, although I fully understand that giving it all up at once will achieve quicker results. Our bodies don't understand what is happening when we suddenly and dramatically change our eating habits like that; we start obsessing about food and what to eat, meal times never come around fast enough, our body goes into starvation mode, and eventually we put all the weight (and more) back on. We feel awful about our failure to lose weight, and the mad cycle starts again.

So, what can we do to lose weight?

If we are serious about seeing a change in ourselves then we will have to make changes. But the changes don't have to be painful and we don't have to go on a diet. The best way to make long lasting change is to change our lifestyle to the one that reflects the size we want to be. A lifestyle is something we become, a behavior that we perpetuate 10 years from today because it is the new normal.

Have you ever started a diet and stopped to go on vacation, then ate everything in sight for the duration of the vacation, and then started the diet again on your return? I have, and it is called madness. How inconvenient is that, constantly worrying about what we eat or don't eat, and stressing over the fact that the whole meal will most likely end up in our hips?

The right lifestyle doesn't care where we are or what we are doing. We might eat and drink more on vacation (or not), but we won't worry about it because our body will easily balance itself on our return. And I'm not talking about food and drink only.

Here are the four things that I believe are key to losing weight:

1. Accept ourselves as we are

If we have a child with a disability or a weight problem we don't love that child any less; yet we stopped loving ourselves a long time ago. Kris Carr, wellness activist and bestselling author, said in her blog[46] that our weight may fluctuate, but our worth never does. I love that.

This is more important than anything else. Ironically, sometimes when we accept ourselves we are not so hung up about losing weight and being a specific size. We might still want to lose weight, but we realize our size doesn't determine who we are or what we can accomplish.

The best gift we can give ourselves is to make peace with ourselves and just accept where we are. Once we do that, we won't care that much about how we look, or at least not with the guilt and

---

[46] http://kriscarr.com/blog/how-to-accept-yourself/

shame that co-exists with not being at our ideal size. Also, we might realize that being super thin is a completely unrealistic goal. Somebody who eats healthy might still be a lot bigger than "Hollywood stars."

Once we release the resistance and negative approach to losing weight, we will see bodily changes more quickly and the weight will drop off much more easily. The more we keep looking at what we don't want, the more we are vibrationally stuck at that point, and the Law of Attraction will ensure that we attract more of the same "I don't like this," "I am fat, I hate my body."

Instead of focusing on those negatives, it is all about finding our energetic vibrational balance. Physically, it is a normal neurological response. When we diet, we become more likely to notice food. Our brains not only notice it, but food begins to look more appetizing and tempting. So the more we try to resist food the harder it gets.

I have dedicated a chapter called Soul Healing (Chapter 26) to understanding the importance of doing the inner work and loving ourselves. Stopping the diet cycle doesn't mean we don't want to change; it means that we can change from a place of feeling powerful and whole as we are.

I always felt that putting on weight was a big failure on my part, but being thin or losing weight doesn't equate to being successful, so why did I feel that being fatter was a failure? Lose weight because you want to feel better and be healthier or more agile, but not because you are not good enough as you are.

If you are loving yourself and accepting where you are, and if your weight still bothers you, the next step is to take an honest look at why you think you put on excess weight.

2. Understand where the stress is coming from

If you overeat due to stress, whatever is causing stress is what you need to try to eliminate from your life. You may try alternative therapies or some of the tools provided in this book. There are many types of stress and many ways to deal with them: Is it a relationship issue? Are you overworked? Are you grieving or recently divorced? Did you have a traumatic experience? Are your children having problems? All of the above? I used to crave huge amounts of chocolate and junk food when I was stressed at work. The answer to my weight problems should have been to find a better coping mechanism than food. Forcing myself to eat salad for lunch achieved nothing.

Your body might also feel stressed if you are not getting enough sleep. Studies show that sleep deprivation causes weight gain. You might want to determine what is causing your inability to sleep, if it is other than just needing to go to bed earlier.

If you think you have a hormonal problem like insulin resistance you will have to deal with that too. As discussed in the previous chapter, Dr. Fung explains that the issue with obesity is that obese people have developed insulin resistance.

3. Adopt better lifestyle habits, slowly

Did you change your eating habits overtime? I was stressed in my pregnancy and I ate a lot. Then I gave birth, I went back to work, and I developed bad habits becoming lazier than I had ever been; not preparing my home made packed lunches (therefore constantly eating out too much and making poor choices), and drinking many "low fat" processed coffees. To top it all off, I was also yo-yo dieting.

If you are just a habit person, changing habits will work because you are just reversing how the issue started. At the end of the day, "dieting" is just about changing your eating habits, but doing so suddenly and drastically. For most people, this is another reason why dieting doesn't work; our brain registers them as such a big task, and such a big change, that it becomes an issue from the start; but small changes won't have so much resistance because you will still eat out and have a piece of cake when you want to.

If you decide to change your habits, you can start slowly by adding one new daily habit. There are a lot of little things that we can do to start the process of moving towards a lifestyle that we want to achieve.

The new habit has to be effortless and consistent over time, or it won't be long lasting. That's how our subconscious is going to pick up a new habit. Remember, we saw in goal setting how our subconscious mind can't compute negatives, so each time we say, "Don't think of an elephant," the first image that comes to mind is, of course, an elephant. It's the same with all the foods that we are being told not to have: our mind is always going to remind us of what we can't have, particularly if we have eaten that food consistently for years. When you say, "I shouldn't have that cake," all you think is cake. Cake. CAKE.

I have found that most people who lost weight and kept it off achieved that slowly, but everybody is different. Some people's bodies are going to accept more easily giving up a lot of things at once, and for others it's going to be a slower process.

As an example of changing a habit, if on your way to work you always grab breakfast from the drive-thru of a fast food restaurant, you would benefit from getting up a bit earlier and making yourself a homemade breakfast with whole foods, like eggs, bacon, and some fruit. Small changes build up over time into new habits. Apart from helping you lose weight, you might enjoy how much better you feel during the morning when you have your homemade breakfast as opposed to the processed meal from the drive-thru.

Some books suggest we keep a journal of everything we eat, because studies prove that by writing it down we will be amazed at how much we eat, and we will tend to eat less. But I think that counting anything in this context is a bad idea. It's like counting portions and calories; I think it will trigger shame or deprivation thoughts which are useless, and put us back to thinking and rethinking about food. If we are listening to our body, we will know when we are getting full. We don't have to count anything, but you may practice mindfulness.

Take time to sit down to eat, taste, and enjoy your food (whatever food that it is on your plate). We consume a lot more food when we just grab a drive-thru meal and eat it on the go, or when we open a packet of cookies and eat them while watching television (instead of sitting down at the table and just eating a normal meal). You might want to read a great book about this called *Mindless Eating: Why We Eat More than We Think*, by Brian Wansink. According to Wansink, the mind makes more than 200 a day food-related decisions, and many of them without pause for actual thought. He argues that we don't have to change what we eat as much as how, and that by making more mindful food-related decisions we can start to eat and live better.

4. Seek help

I'm not a weight loss expert, but it is my understanding that in some cases, for alcoholics, for example, it is appropriate to give up all alcohol at once. In the same way, an anorexic, a morbidly obese, or a bulimic person might require or desire professional support. If you think you have a serious issue, please seek medical advice.

◆ ◆ ◆

Whatever path you take in the end, try to avoid letting diets and thinking about food take too much of your time. I don't have weight loss or exercise goals anymore. Instead, I consider eating well, slowly changing my habits, and exercising, all part of my daily existence. I try to make better choices without overly thinking about them. I don't eat well all the time (I love eating out and nice chocolate desserts), but I feel great and I have lost weight without dieting.

I'm not worried about what I eat or my weight anymore, and that on its own has brought me a lot of peace.

The bottom line is: A lifestyle is forever. Mike Tyson said that everybody has a plan until they get punched in the mouth. Life's ups and downs are inevitable. We came here to enjoy life the best we could, not to add misery and restrictions to an already challenging existence.

On the subject of losing weight, I recommend four great books:

- *How to Have Your Cake and Your Skinny Jeans Too: Stop Binge Eating, Overeating & Dieting for Good*, by Josie Spinardi
- *Brain Over Binge: Why I Was Bulimic, Why Conventional Therapy Didn't Work, and How I Recovered for Good*, by Kathryn Hansen

- The *Obesity Code: Unlocking the Secrets of Weight Loss,* by Jason Fung, MD
- *Mini Habits for Weight Loss: Stop Dieting, Form New Habits. Change Your Lifestyle Without Suffering,* by Stephen Guise

24

The Role of Exercise

*Exercise to stimulate, not to annihilate. The world wasn't formed
in a day, and neither were we. Set goals and build upon them.*

LEE HANEY

THERE IS A difference between the health benefits of exercise,
which are multiple, and the weight loss benefits of exercise,
which are limited.

Exercise for weight loss

I always thought that if I exercised a lot more I would lose all the
weight I wanted. But I have learned that exercise doesn't play such a
big role after all.[47] The benefits of exercise are huge, and I will go into
that in a moment; but generally, exercise doesn't function well as a
weight loss tool. There are two reasons why:

1. Our body always seeks to balance itself, we learned that in the
   previous chapter. It is called homeostasis. For example, we

---

[47] https://www.sciencedaily.com/releases/2017/02/170203163857.htm

always keep an internal temperature of 98.7 degrees Fahrenheit regardless of the temperature outside.

One study,[48] *Hunter-Gatherer Energetics and Human Obesity,* found that although indigenous people in Tanzania (Hadza hunter-gatherers) walked twice as far as Westerners, their daily energy expenditure was no different than that of Westerners, suggesting that our bodies adapt to our activity levels and find ways to keep our overall energy expenditure in check. Basically, the body adapts to conserve energy and survive.

Extracted from the study:

The similarity in TEE {total energy expenditure} among Hadza hunter-gatherers and Westerners suggests that even dramatic differences in lifestyle may have a negligible effect on TEE, and is consistent with the view (…) that differences in obesity prevalence between populations result primarily from differences in energy intake rather than expenditure.

This means that what we eat is far more important than how much we exercise.

In another study[49], Danish researches trained a group of 18 men and nine women to run a marathon over 18 months. After that period, the men group lost an average of 5 pounds each, but the women group didn't lose any weight at all. This study reminds me of the importance of doing things because of the joy they will bring to our lives in the process of doing them. Gym attendance rates are poor compared to the number of paying members because the primary reason for attending a gym is usually to lose weight or become more fit, not necessarily because of the fun involved. Our soul is always going to

---

[48] http://dx.doi.org/10.1371/journal.pone.0040503

[49] https://www.ncbi.nlm.nih.gov/pubmed/2744924

push us to do joyful things, which is why it's so hard to go the gym if we don't enjoy it. If you set a goal of running a marathon because you want to lose weight, but you barely tolerate running, you might end up being very disappointed. But if you want to run a marathon for the huge accomplishment that it represents and because you love running, then this totally enhances your vibration and helps you at many levels, because exercise is a great tool to help us feel better.

2. Weight is not the result of calories in versus calories out. This is because the total amount of calories we burn each day is the sum of:

    a. The calories we need for our body to function. This is called our Basal Metabolic Rate (BMR): breathing, pumping blood, maintaining vital organs, etc. This is basically the amount of calories we burn while we do nothing (rest).
    b. Calories used in digestion and absorption of food.
    c. Exercise.

Dr. Fung says that the problem with assuming that exercise is the way to burn calories and lose weight is that the BMR does not stay stable, that is, our body some days might need more or fewer calories to function; and as we have seen earlier, our bodies adapt to our new routines. We might exercise more to try to create a caloric deficit but our BMR might also be decreasing (we are burning fewer calories while resting, particularly if our body feels threatened).

Exercise represents a very small part of the total amount of our total energy expenditure; most of the calories we consume are used by our body just to function normally.

Our BMR depends on many factors (the higher it is, the more calories it burns while resting), including:

- Age: The older a person is, the slower his BMR is. You are likely to put on more weight as you grow older just because your BMR slows down.

- Gender: Females have been found to have a 2% to 12% lower BMR than males. The difference is more marked in older age groups.
- Climate and body temperature: If you work or exercise in very cold weather, it takes energy to keep the body warm. Mountain climbers lose enormous amounts of weight while scaling the tallest peaks in the world because their body needs far more energy simply to exist. Extreme temperatures can have a drastic effect on how calories are expended by the body (and thus, how much fat is stored).
- Pregnancy: Pregnancy increases the BMR, but this varies considerably among women.
- Diet: Fasting lowers BMR. Implications of fasting on BMR have been proven in multiple studies. Did you know that women's periods can stop with over enthusiastic dieting? Our bodies will shut down to conserve energy.
- Health: Fever, illness, or injury may increase resting metabolic rate. Menopause might also affect metabolism.
- Drugs: Those used to treat hormonal problems like hyper-thyroidism can also affect BMR. Some people report putting on weight just because they are taking specific medicines.

Also, usually we are hungrier after exercising.[50] It is a normal hormonal response, so if we end up eating more it will be very difficult to cause any significant amount of weight loss.

In conclusion, we have very little control over our BMR, and it is very hard to create a significant caloric deficit through exercise because the body will always try to compensate.

However, there are many people who have become very healthy while exercising, particularly over the long term. Studies have proven that people who are fit and healthy are usually very active and have been active for a long time. Long-term exercising and being active has

---

[50] https://www.sciencedaily.com/releases/2008/06/080617142925.htm

been associated with people who love those activities for the sake of the activities, not to lose weight.

Exercise for health

Exercise is excellent for health. Multiple studies[51] have shown the long term benefits of physical activity on many diseases, including coronary heart disease, Type 2 diabetes, and dementia.

Exercise has also been proven to help us feel happier by improving our mood. When we are exercising, our body releases chemicals called endorphins, which trigger positive feelings in the body, similar to that of morphine. (This feeling is known as "runner's high.") Endorphins have been proven to act as pain relievers and sedatives.

Exercise can help you with the following:

- Stress reduction
- Boosted self-esteem
- Mental clarity and productivity
- Sleep improvements
- Body toning
- Happiness
- Addiction control
- Detoxification in your body of mind-altering chemicals when sweating
- Improved blood flow and oxygen movement, particularly with aerobic exercise

In conclusion, exercise plays a very small role in our quest to lose weight. Our bodies are designed to adapt and conserve energy, and our

---

[51] BMC Public Health, Reiner et al. BMC Public Health 2013, 13:813

http://bmcpublichealth.biomedcentral.com/articles/10.1186/1471-2458-13-813

BMR fluctuates. However, exercise is vital for long term health, and it will help us to tone up and feel amazing at all levels.

In Part III: Healing Body and Soul, I aimed to discuss how to achieve overall physical and emotional healing. This chapter on exercise concludes the content around healing and finding well-being in the physical body.

In the next couple of chapters we will discuss how we can continue to achieve emotional well-being, by learning how we can heal difficult relationships and loving ourselves.

25

Healing Difficult Relationships

Conflict exists strictly as an opportunity to raise our consciousness

CARL JUNG

W E ENTER INTO significant relationships to work out our major issues. We choose our partners, parents, bosses, and anybody else in a significant relationship with us because they resonate with the same underlying emotional patterns that we hold.

Our relationships hold the key to something we need to resolve and heal. There is a valuable lesson in every difficult or painful relationship. If you do not see the lesson, it doesn't mean there isn't one. Many of these karmic relationships, often love-hate relationships, are from past lifetimes which our soul brings back into our lives so that we can finally resolve, absolve the karma, and move on.

As well as coming to learn our own lessons, we also come to Earth to play a part in the drama of other's people lessons. We chose and joined in life with our parents, siblings, spouses, and close friends. There is always a reason to be at the end of pain or pleasure from a close relative. This is the soul's way of pushing us to the next level in our evolution.

All the painful and traumatic experiences we create in a relationship are carried in our soul memory and on to our next relationship. When we try to turn away from a relationship without fulfilling our contract, we might be predisposed to attract another one with similar traits. This is why we seem to re-create the same scenario repeatedly. When we enter a new relationship we project all our hurts and disappointments from the previous ones, and then we leave it before we learn the lesson. This is one of the main reasons divorce rates increase for second and third marriages. In most cases, we are attempting to walk away from an aspect of ourselves that we don't like.

The Emerald Tablet of Hermes Trismegistus is a short work that contains a phrase that is well-known in occult circles: "As above, so below. As within, so without." It is the second principle of the Kybalion, the Principle of Correspondence: As above, so below.

"As within, so without" means that what goes on in our lives (externally) is a reflection of what is going on in our inner world. The universe and our surroundings rearrange themselves to bring us what we believe, and to reflect our existing reality.

The Law of Reflection

The Law of Reflection is tied to "As within, so without." What goes on internally is mirrored back to us. Everything is a reflection. We need to look at what the mirror of people and life is telling us; and if we don't like it, we need to try to make the necessary inner changes. We should never try to change anyone else, because they are reflecting us.

Have you ever wondered why some personality traits bother you greatly and others don't? It is not chance; it is because the things you notice are the things you have to work on. Change the inner self and you will start seeing results. The same principle applies to the traits you like in people; they mirror back the parts that you like about yourself. A very kind person might see a lot of kindness around them.

Soul mates and romantic relationships

Much has been said and written about our "other half" or "soul mates." The notion of the "other half," as in literally needing somebody else to be "whole," is a very disempowering statement. It is not healthy or healing from a spiritual point of view because it makes us dependent on something or someone outside of us to achieve happiness and fulfillment. Our "soul mate" breaks up with us and we think we won't be happy ever again. There is also a misconception that only one soul mate exists.

Sometimes we enter relationships with the false expectation that others can complete us, but they can't. The key ingredient for relationship success is to not need it, but to be wholly complete unto ourselves. If our partners are not whole unto themselves, they won't be able to supply what they don't have either.

It is not necessary to have a relationship to be, do, or have what you intend, but of course it is a desirable experience to have someone with whom to share your life.

There is only one important relationship, and that is you with yourself. All romantic relationships must begin with us. Once we are happy and complete with ourselves, then we will be able to have all the other relationships we want. The same applies to non-romantic relationships. The more desperate we are to attract friendship, the more we repel it. The happier we are with our circumstances, the more we attract goodness. We have to take care of ourselves first and foremost; nothing else will happen until that is done.

Healing relationships

Ho'oponopono

Ho'oponopono is a Hawaiian method for healing. It means "to make right" or "to correct." It is based on the understanding that anything that happens to us is entirely our responsibility, which doesn't mean it's our fault, but it means that we are responsible for healing ourselves in order to heal whatever or whomever it is that appears to us as a problem.

A Hawaiian psychiatrist named Dr. Ihaleakala Hew Len discovered a technique that helped his mentally ill patients get better. He took on their pains and problems as if they were his own, and worked on healing those issues within himself. Dr. Len would think of his client, take his file case, and repeat over and over:

"I love you. I am sorry. Please forgive me. Thank you."

Ho'oponopono works because we are all energetically connected and, as we have seen in the Law of Reflection, the world is a reflection of what is going on inside us. If we are experiencing upset or imbalance we need to look inside ourselves, not outside at the object we perceive to be causing our problem. Ho'oponopono asserts that every stress, imbalance, or illness can be corrected just by working on ourselves.

I have used Ho'oponopono many times with my personal relationship issues and I have experienced great results. I think of the person I'm having a relationship problem with, I picture him or her clearly in my mind, and then I say to the person in my mind, "I love you. I'm sorry. Please forgive me. Thank you." It doesn't matter who started the argument, who said what, who is "right" or "wrong." I do this regardless of who I perceive to be "at fault." If we start the blaming game, we will never be in the vibration of the solution.

Do you prefer to be right or happy? I have learned to let go of the need to be right. I ask myself, why do I feel the need to defend my beliefs? Why does it matter so much to me what anybody else believes? Even when we are "right," our spiritual evolution doesn't benefit from our rightness; it benefits from our eagerness to let go of stuff that is not important. Being right is not important. When we leave our physical body, the fact that we were right will be absolutely irrelevant.

Use visualization

Visualize white light, or love, going out from your heart to them. If, for example, you want somebody to be kinder to you, then instead of criticizing them – which they will pick up energetically – you can visualize them talking to you more nicely next time. We can always control our vibrational output.

You might do this in conjunction with Ho'oponopono.

Visit your troubled relationships in your sleep

You can talk to people's higher self directly. Just ask your higher self, guides, or angels to take you to see him (or her). Explain in your head, or write a letter, what you want to achieve with that discussion. People are more receptive to solutions when they can see the higher picture (on a soul level). You might not remember the conversation, but it will happen, and it will be recorded in the subconscious mind of each person to act upon, as needed. In the previous example, you might find that the person becomes less aggressive towards you, or stops picking on you altogether.

Put yourself in their shoes

Look at things from both sides and make your best effort to understand where the other person is coming from. It is often said that two people don't fight if one doesn't want to.

Most of the time people don't mean to harm or hurt us; they are in our world for many reasons:

1. They are simply there to facilitate our growth. The quicker we are able to understand what we are learning from a person or situation, the quicker we can leave it. (For example, some people come into our life to play out our beliefs. If we believe

we are lonely and nobody loves us, we will attract a relationship with someone who betrays us, or leaves us.)

2. People sometimes don't know another way to behave than to
   get angry. That is their way to vocalize their pain, or they are at
   a stage in their soul evolution where they don't know a better
   way to behave. Confucius said: *"To be wronged is nothing unless you
   continue to remember it."*

3. They are also hurting, and they might be feeling that they can't
   get through to you. Do you listen – truly listen – to what your
   partner, friend, or parent has to say? Do you watch how you
   say things to them? Do you have to be right every time? There
   are always two sides to the story. Watch your own behavior.
   We all know how and when to push each other's buttons.
   Don't make things worse; you don't have to fight and lower
   yourself to the same level. Make sure you are in a good place
   and everything else won't matter to you so much.

Know when to walk away

There is never a good enough excuse to tolerate being physically or
verbally abused, so make sure to stand up for yourself and ask your
guides and angels for guidance on your next steps. Change is
uncomfortable. Leaving something we know, even something that
makes us miserable, still means leaving the familiar and embarking on
the unknown.

Sometimes the best way to avoid negative influence from others is
to remove ourselves physically, mentally, and emotionally. This applies
to all people: partners, family members, and friends.

Sometimes we convince ourselves that we have to stay in a
broken relationship because we believe we share karma, and we have
been told by our parents, or other authority figures, that the right thing
to do is "to work things out" and "compromise." Our parents might
have been conditioned to think that marriage is forever, but they don't

and can't know the higher picture as to why we entered into that relationship. Make choices for yourself; nobody else has walked or will walk in your shoes.

Relationships sometimes end because one of the partners has mastered one of the primary lessons they came to achieve. Not all relationships are contracted or desired to be long lasting. I'm not saying either we have to leave at the smallest problem, or that compromising is not good. What I'm saying is that you don't need to prolong a relationship when you are suffering. We didn't come to Earth to suffer.

It is incorrect to think that suffering will pay our karma back and at some point we will be free to move on. It has the opposite effect: By staying in a painful relationship we might be avoiding the life lesson we came to master; for example, to stand up for ourselves. We can't work out karma "together." The problem you have with your partner might just be a way to show you that you can be well and content by yourself. Resolving karma and overcoming our life lessons are things we do on our own. We only have responsibility for ourselves and our small children.

If you hang out too often with people who make you feel depressed, who don't treat you well, who constantly complain about the economy and say that all their problems are somebody else's fault, then it is probably best to move away from them. I'm not talking about removing them altogether, or not being there for a friend in need of help; I'm talking about choosing to spend more time with people who support you, uplift you, make you happy, and empower you. I'm talking about a mutually beneficial relationship. You give and receive.

The Principle of Association says that we are influenced by those around us. If we hang out with people who are kind, helpful, and have an overall positive attitude, it is more likely that we will develop those traits.

Inner peace means releasing attachments to everything, from having a person act the way you want or to having the world work the way you expect. When you let go of those attachments, you will find your life working even better than you could have expected or planned.

Cutting the ties that bind

Cords are emotional strands of energy that form regardless of time or space. When we consistently direct our thoughts and energy to a particular person, place, or thing, we begin to establish an energetic cord connecting us to that object or person. We saw in Chapter 2 that we all know when someone is staring at us – we feel it. We are all interconnected in the Field of Consciousness, and thoughts travel inside the field, connecting one to another.

When we have constant thoughts about someone, it is likely that they are connecting with us in some way. They might be thinking about us, or it could also be our own repetitive obsessive thoughts, because the more we concentrate on a thought the more we attract the same type of thoughts. The more we send our energy to somebody, and the more we think about them, the thicker and bigger the cord becomes. The stronger the emotional connection, the stronger the bonding.

We also create energy cords when we make conscious or subconscious vows, contracts, or promises with other people. It is particularly strong in parent/child, husband/wife, past lovers, siblings, doctor/patient, teacher/student, past and present friends, and enemies.

Cords can be formed quickly when we become dependent on people. Healthy cords create a nurturing sharing of information and energy; for example, the cords created between mothers and their young children. Unhealthy cords can be a way to gain control of another person, but at no point are we victims of circumstance; we won't have unhealthy cords unless, for example, we agreed to be the controller, or the one who is controlled.

Energy follows thought through intent. If you have a situation where your ex doesn't leave you in peace (whether physically or you feel it energetically), you should consider cutting the cords to that person.

Cords are formed and linked through our chakras. You might have multiple cords attached to one person; for example, one in the second chakra which represents sexuality and desire, and another one in your solar plexus (third chakra), which represents the seat of your emotions.

We can cut the cords to our husband or wife and still be married (or friends). You might want to cut the unhealthy, controlling, interdependent behavior if that is something that you think is an issue for you. Sometimes we have heart chakra interdependencies; for example, marrying for money, or out of loneliness and insecurity. When we love for the sake of loving, unconditionally, we create healthy cords that won't need cutting or healing.

In the end, cords can be very draining. You might be divorced (separated) physically but not energetically, and it will benefit both parties to cut the cords that bind them; this enhances your relationships and brings more joy into your life.

Phyllis Krystal developed a method to cut the cords to anyone or anything. Her book, *Cutting the Ties that Bind: Growing Up and Moving On,* contains exercises that will help you free yourself from unhealthy cords.

I also recommend *The Healing Power of Mind: Simple Meditation Exercises for Health, Well-Being, and Enlightenment,* by Tulku Thondup (Specifically, Chapter 8, Exercise 11: Cutting the Bonds of Unpleasant Relationships).

A final note about unhealthy cords: don't become afraid of them and feel that you are doomed until you cut them. I believe we can heal from unhealthy cords without intentionally cutting them. The better we get physically and emotionally, the healthier and stronger our aura becomes.

We can choose a myriad of ways to feel better. For example, we can improve our thoughts, the food we eat, or the company we keep.

We can have more play time; we can let go or forgive, and we can generally become happier. Cutting the ties that bind us is just another tool to help us heal our relationships and ourselves.

26

Soul Healing

A sad soul can kill you quicker than a germ

ALBERT SCHWEITZER
(NOBEL PEACE PRIZE WINNER, 1952)

WE ARE ON Earth to heal the deep wounds within our own being, to evolve and grow in consciousness. If we haven't attended to ourselves first we can't help others, or the earth. When we take extreme care of ourselves and seek inner peace, everything else falls into place because everything we want is in our vibration, and not just in our actions. Unless we change how we are, we will always get what we got.

Happiness is not the result of achieving goals, getting things done, or winning the lottery. Happiness is a state of mind and a feeling of inner peace. The better we feel inside, the better our life will become.

The role of forgiveness

Life becomes easier when you learn to accept an apology you never got

ROBERT BRAULT

I want to address what I perceive to be a misconception around the role of forgiveness. We are told we need to forgive anybody who has hurt us because:

- It is the path to healing
- It is what spiritual people do
- God would forgive and expects us to do so
- It is the right thing to do
- We will find freedom
- [Fill in the blank.]

I agree it is important to forgive, but only when we wish to and are ready to do so. Understanding the Law of Attraction, and the agreements we made in our planning sessions prior to coming to Earth, has helped me to understand the reasons behind hurtful people and events. But forgiveness only came as a byproduct of that understanding, not because "I had to forgive."

We don't have to love unconditionally regardless of how people behave or who they are.

The fact that the soul doesn't die doesn't make war right. If somebody is being abusive, it is not right to allow the abuse to continue. When we are ready we will forgive, but we should not push ourselves against what we feel. We have a lot to gain when we genuinely feel that way, but we shouldn't feel we have to forgive if, in our heart, we know we haven't, or can't.

Even worse, don't feel guilty because you have been told, "shame on you for not forgiving." If you don't want to forgive don't, if you want to be angry, sad, and vulnerable, then feel that. There is a normal progression in our emotions, and it is healthy to naturally follow them. It is similar to the process of grieving; after losing a loved one it is good to allow yourself to be sad and grieve.

After a negative experience, at first you might feel powerless and depressed. You might follow that with anger and a desire for revenge, followed by pessimism about life and all things. Slowly, as the time passes, you might move up the emotional scale and feel hopeful that there is a way out. Eventually, you see the higher picture and analyze the situation from your soul's perspective, who knows what it is doing.

All difficult situations arose to help us on our path. I believe I chose to experience a difficult childhood and years of bullying because I would never have had such an interest in self help books, or achieved what I have done in my life as a result of the knowledge that I have gained. I have always been looking for answers to soothe myself, and I believe I'm a more improved person because of everything I have learnt in the process. Rumi, a 13th century poet and Sufi mystic said that the wound is the place where the light enters you.

It is healing for our body and soul to seek and find forgiveness; we let go of ideas of revenge, we see a reduction in our stress levels and feelings of despair, our depression lifts, and our relationships improve. When we are resentful, we keep ourselves stuck in a vibrational pattern that doesn't help us find peace or achieve our goals. ("I'm down because of this, or that.") Success vibrates at a high frequency, and feeling and being a victim vibrates at a much lower one.

I wish the bullies well now, but it has taken me a long time to genuinely feel that way; I carried that pain for many years. In my mid-thirties I realized that by not letting go of my childhood bullying experience, I was still letting the bullies hurt me. By not forgiving, the only one still suffering was me.

Nelson Mandela, winner of the Nobel Peace Prize, said it so eloquently:

*"Resentment is like drinking poison and
then hoping it will kill your enemies"*

Forgive and love yourself

I read somewhere that if your compassion does not include yourself, then it is incomplete. I find it easier to forgive others than to forgive myself, but we would not be on Earth if we were perfect. If we had mastered every lesson, and every aspect of ourselves, we would be on another planet, but not here. There is no point in looking back at our past and giving ourselves a hard time over what we did or didn't do, or how we behaved. It is beneficial to learn from that if we don't like what we did, but there is no point feeling guilty and punishing ourselves about it.

We did the very best we could at that time with the information we had. If we could have done better, we would have. I have done things I'm not proud of, I have said things that I would rather not remember, and I have been childish and selfish. But what we did or didn't do has no bearing on what we can accomplish today. Nobody other than ourselves is going to punish us.

Alan Cohen, in his book *I Had It All the Time: When Self Improvement Gives Way to Ecstasy*, writes:

> Give yourself the release you hope to receive from other people. Do no wait for God or others to pardon you. God has already pardoned you – it is you who need to pardon yourself (A course in miracles suggests that "God does not forgive because He has never condemned.")

Accepting ourselves

Today's society is plagued with images of beauty and happiness that are not real. Unrealistic images can make us feel inadequate, and worse, in need of fixing. They can totally disconnect us from our true needs. They lead us to believe that a thin body and being famous equals happiness forever.

Self acceptance is a form of self love and self forgiveness. Love is the biggest magnet for positive changes in our life. If we love and accept ourselves for who we are, we will attract circumstances and people who reflect our self love.

Acceptance also means accepting where we are now. Find reasons to be grateful for who you are now, not who you think you should be. We deserve to be, do, and have what we want simply because we chose to come to Earth; that is our birthright. Our worthiness is not based on how much we have, where we were born, or where we live now, what car we drive, our weight, or any other factors. It might sound simple, but it is really that simple.

People can place no higher value upon us than we place upon ourselves. Ultimately, *we* are the ones who determine our own value. If you were told that you wouldn't amount to anything, decide now that you are worth it and expect great things to happen!

27

Life Reminders

Things don't change. You change the way of looking, that's all

CARLOS CASTANEDA

WE HAVE ARRIVED at the end of the book; I hope you liked it and found it useful.

I would like to finish with 33 life reminders:

1. You have come to this world on purpose. You knew what you were doing, and you were eager to take the trip. You have a specific destiny to fulfill. If you follow your joy, you can find it.

2. Your own spiritual growth and inner peace is the greatest contribution you can make to yourself and the world. Your life will improve to the extent that you do.

3. Take action to change your life and make a commitment to yourself: Know that you can make your life work.

4. You can bring things into reality more quickly by imagining that you already have them. That includes physical things as well as non-material ones, such as feeling confident, or having more compassion. Remember the power of your mind to create abundance and heal your body.

5. Silence is golden. You are only hurting yourself when you are directing your anger and hate toward others. You will feel more at peace when you only say things that serve people in some way.

6. Accept that everybody is on different levels of evolution, but nobody is better or worse because of it.

7. You can't please everybody. People will have an opinion about what you do or don't do, and they will judge you if they want; but what they do is none of your business.

8. You can't change anybody, but you can consciously choose what and who you surround yourself with.

9. You don't earn respect. People are going to be respectful to you or not depending on who *they* are, not who you are; but you can stand up for yourself and you can choose your reaction to them.

10. Keep an open mind. We don't know better than anybody else because we don't have the higher picture.

11. Believe in yourself and your ability to create the life you want. Nothing can stop you except your thoughts and beliefs. Richard Bach, bestselling author of *Jonathan Livingston Seagull*, writes, "Sooner or later, those who win are those who think they can."

12. You have the right to change your mind, and you have the right to not explain your decisions.

13. You will feel better when you don't judge, because you will not feel judged. When we judge ourselves or others, we are failing to see the higher picture.

14. Pay attention to the way you feel, and deliberately choose thoughts – about everything – that feel good to you when you think of them. Seek to have thoughts and do things that make you feel good.

15. Your attitude and mindset are important. You can be poor and happy, or wealthy and unhappy. You don't have to wait to achieve your goals to feel happy.

16. Don't waste your pain. Choose to grow from your experiences and come out stronger and wiser because of them. Learn from your mistakes, apologize, or find another way, but don't beat yourself up. Your compassion has to include you.

17. Your size, weight, or height does not define you. You don't need to change; you just need to love and accept yourself. You will then attract circumstances and people who reflect your self-love.

18. No one has ever gotten healthier by feeling worse about themselves, nor have they lived a day longer by worrying.

19. Take care of your business and nobody else's. Remember, the way you perceive something might not be the reality of it. There is a story about a young couple who moved into a neighborhood. The next morning while they are eating breakfast the woman sees her neighbor hanging out the laundry and says, "The laundry isn't very clean; she doesn't know how to wash correctly. Perhaps she needs better laundry soap." Her husband looks on, remaining silent. Every time her neighbor hangs her laundry out to dry, the young woman makes the same comments. A month later, the woman is surprised to see a nice clean laundry on the line and says to her husband "Look, she's finally learned how to wash correctly.

Do you think someone taught her?" Her husband replies, "I got up early this morning and cleaned our windows."

20. Everything will pass, it always does. Do not give permanent reality to temporary situations.

21. You don't have to do everything on your own. Seek help. Talk to trusted friends, family, or your physician. Call a help line. Enroll in a 12-step program. Ask your guides and angels to show you the clues to your next steps. Write them a letter. You might notice a song on the radio; listen to the lyrics. You might see an advert in a magazine. Your guides and angels will point you in the right direction, but you need to pay attention to the clues and take action. Notice what you notice!

22. Cleaning and tidying your house, car, office and your belongings (including your handbags and wallets), will help you at all levels.

23. It is said life is the most difficult exam but we fail because we try to copy each other without realizing we are all sitting different exams. Know that you can't fail, and that you don't have to keep up with anybody else.

24. Don't take yourself too seriously, and remember what is important for you.

25. Sleep, rest, proper nourishment, play time, and meditation will always help your physical and emotional well-being. Get as much of them as you can. Don't ignore your body's signals.

26. As Robert Brault said, life becomes easier when you learn to accept an apology you never got. Forgiveness heals body and soul.

27. Give yourself permission to stop rescuing others. We disempower people when we take on their stuff. You are not responsible for making other people's life work.

28. It is not possible to give from an empty cup. Fill your cup first and create the life you desire.

29. It will serve your evolution to detach yourself from situations that are disordered and stressful; follow your intuition to know when to walk away.

30. Take calculated risks. In the end, you will be more disappointed with what you didn't do than with what you did.

31. Remember you are not here to be perfect or to think positive all the time. You will have days when you cry, or feel disappointment and hurt. You will have days when you feel depressed and fed up with life and everybody else. That is what it makes you normal, and human. It is okay. But also remember...

32. You can pick yourself up from where you are; you have done it before, and you can do it now. You have felt like this before, and you came through it. You can pull yourself together and make the most of life now.

33. Living on Earth is not easy, but you knew you could find your path to joy, so you took the chance. All possibilities will be open to you when you listen to your intuition and follow your excitement. Acting on your inner guidance will bring you closer to your divine right of living with joy.

*Will you fall into forgetting again? Of course, and
you will awaken again. Each time you remember, the delight
of your heart will explode into a million twinkling stars.*

EMMANUEL'S BOOK III

Questions? Comments?

If you have found this book useful, could you please take a moment to leave a review on Amazon[52]? Reviews are the best way to help a book grow and be discovered by others so they, too, can be helped.

And if you have any questions or comments, or if you would like me to expand on a specific topic in the next edition of this book, please email me at roser@rosersegarra.com.

Thank you!

---

[52] http://amzn.to/2f1Aa05

NOTES

Made in the USA
Middletown, DE
06 August 2018